Test Book

EXPLORING PLANET EARTH

Prentice Hall
Englewood Cliffs, New Jersey
Needham, Massachusetts

Test Book

PRENTICE HALL SCIENCE
Exploring Planet Earth

ISBN 0-13-987231-0

7 8 9 10 96 95

Prentice Hall
A Division of Simon & Schuster
Englewood Cliffs, New Jersey 07632

Contents

To the Teacher

This *Test Book* contains all the testing materials that accompany the student textbook. The testing materials are divided into three parts:

CHAPTER TEST

Every chapter in the student textbook has an accompanying Chapter Test. These tests are meant to test both factual recall and concept development. Each Chapter Test is divided into five sections. These sections are Multiple Choice, Completion, True or False, Using Science Skills, and Essay. An Answer Key for each Chapter Test is also included.

COMPUTER TEST BANK TEST

Every chapter in the student textbook has an accompanying Computer Test Bank Chapter Test. These tests are meant to test both factual recall and concept development. Each Computer Test Bank Test is divided into five sections. These sections are Multiple Choice, True or False, Completion, Using Science Skills, and Critical Thinking and Application. An Answer Key for each Test Bank Test is also included.

You may choose to copy the entire Computer Test Bank Chapter Test. A complete User's Guide is included in the disk package. Using your computer and the test disks, you can print out your own chapter test, quiz, midterm, or final exam, selecting questions from the Test Bank as well as adding your own. An Illustration Master for each visual question in the Test Bank Test is included after the questions. These Illustration Masters are to be used when you print out a test from your printer. An Answer Key for each test is also included.

The APPLE, IBM, and MAC disks for the ***Prentice Hall Science*** Computer Test Banks include questions from the Computer Test Bank for all 19 titles in the program.

For current prices and ordering information call your Customer Service Representative toll free 1-800-848-9500. Refer to the appropriate ISBN number below.

Item (ISBN #)	Description
0-13-987686-3	Apple 5 1/4-inch Program and Data Disks for the *Prentice Hall Science* Computer Test Bank (User's Guide included)
0-13-987702-9	IBM 5 1/4-inch Program and Data Disks for the *Prentice Hall Science* Computer Test Bank (User's Guide included)
0-13-986944-1	IBM 3 1/2-inch Program and Data Disks for the *Prentice Hall Science* Computer Test Bank (User's Guide included)
0-13-987694-4	MAC 3 1/2-inch Program and Data Disks for the *Prentice Hall Science* Computer Test Bank (User's Guide included)

PERFORMANCE-BASED TESTS

A set of Performance-Based Tests is included in this *Test Book.* Performance-Based Tests are designed to test a student's thinking and problem-solving abilities and are not meant to be content dependent. Although the tests have been designed to be given when the student has completed the textbook, you may prefer to give individual tests after particular chapters in the textbook. If you like, you may incorporate some of the Performance-Based Tests into your Chapter Test.

Performance-Based Tests are given at workstations. All materials the student needs are placed at the workstation, along with the worksheets the student must fill out. Students must be told in advance the amount of time they will have at each workstation. Make sure students understand that they must leave the workstation exactly as they found it.

Contents

CHAPTER 1 ■ Earth's Atmosphere

Name ______________________ Class ____________ Date __________

Chapter Test

CHAPTER 1 ■ Earth's Atmosphere

MULTIPLE CHOICE

Write the letter of the correct answer on the line at the left.

_____ **1.** The approximate percent of oxygen in the atmosphere is
a. less than 1 percent. c. 78 percent.
b. 21 percent. d. 99 percent.

_____ **2.** The gas removed from the atmosphere by plants during the food-making process is
a. oxygen. c. carbon dioxide.
b. nitrogen. d. ozone.

_____ **3.** A gas that varies between 0 percent and 4 percent of the atmosphere in different places is
a. nitrogen. c. methane.
b. oxygen. d. water vapor.

_____ **4.** Strong eastward winds that blow around the Earth in the lower stratosphere are called
a. the jet stream. c. solar winds.
b. convection currents. d. radiation belts.

_____ **5.** The solar wind is made up of
a. oxygen. c. nitrogen.
b. ions. d. all the gases in the Earth's atmosphere.

_____ **6.** The highest layer of the atmosphere is the
a. thermosphere. c. stratosphere.
d. troposphere. d. mesosphere.

_____ **7.** The zone that separates the mesosphere from the layer below it is called the
a. stratopause. c. mesopause.
b. tropopause. d. thermopause.

_____ **8.** Solar flares interfere with radio communications because of the effect of the flares on the
a. exosphere. c. mesosphere.
b. ionosphere. d. stratosphere.

_____ **9.** Chemical reactions triggered by sunlight in the Earth's early atmosphere produced large quantities of
a. hydrogen. c. nitrogen.
b. carbon dioxide. d. all of these.

_____ **10.** Ozone is made up of atoms of
a. nitrogen. c. oxygen.
b. hydrogen. d. carbon.

COMPLETION

Complete each statement on the line at the left.

_____________ 1. The envelope of gases surrounding the Earth is called the _____.

_____________ 2. Living things need nitrogen to make complex nitrogen compounds called _____.

_____________ 3. The downward push of the atmosphere is called _____.

_____________ 4. The lowest layer of the atmosphere is called the _____.

_____________ 5. Bands of high radiation trapped by the Earth's magnetosphere are called the _____.

TRUE OR FALSE

Determine whether each statement is true or false. If it is true, write T. If it is false, change the underlined word or words to make the statement true.

_____ _____________ 1. <u>Ozone</u> absorbs harmful ultraviolet radiation from the sun.

_____ _____________ 2. The most abundant gas in the atmosphere is <u>nitrogen</u>.

_____ _____________ 3. Air pressure <u>increases</u> as distance from the Earth's surface increases.

_____ _____________ 4. The upper <u>mesosphere</u> is the coldest region of the atmosphere.

_____ _____________ 5. During respiration, living things chemically combine <u>carbon dioxide</u> with food.

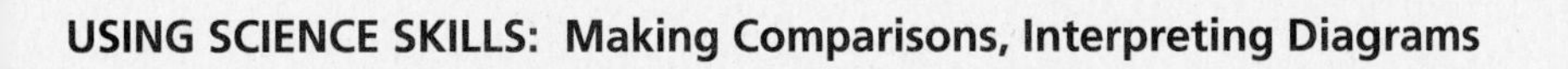
Name ______ Class ______ Date ______

USING SCIENCE SKILLS: Making Comparisons, Interpreting Diagrams

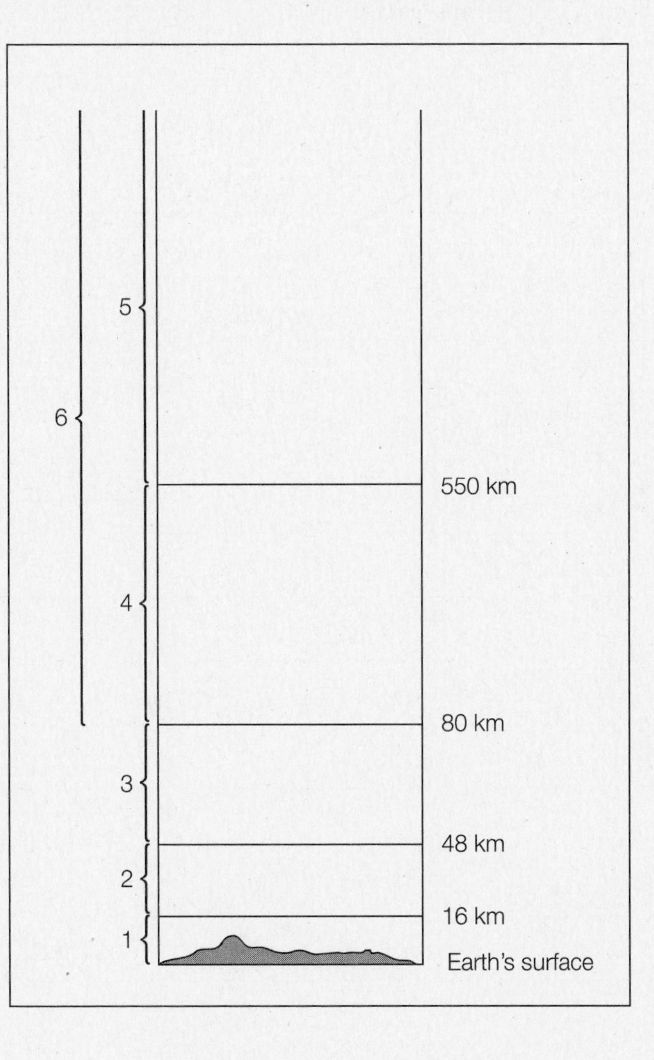

1. What are the names of the layers of the atmosphere labeled 1 through 6?

   1. ______ 4. ______
   2. ______ 5. ______
   3. ______ 6. ______

2. What does the line between layers 1 and 2 represent? ______

   The line between 2 and 3? ______

3. How does temperature vary with increasing altitude within layer 1? ______

   Layer 2? ______ Layer 3? ______ Layer 4? ______

4. In which layer is the jet stream located? ______ In which layer are radio waves bounced back toward the Earth? ______

ESSAY

Write a brief paragraph discussing each of the following statements or questions.

1. Describe the nature, location, and importance of the Van Allen radiation belts.

2. Describe the characteristics of the mesosphere and its role in protecting the Earth from meteoroids.

3. Describe the production and use of oxygen and carbon dioxide by living things.

4. What might happen if pollution of the Earth's atmosphere continues? What can be done to prevent air pollution?

Answer Key

CHAPTER 1 ■ Earth's Atmosphere

MULTIPLE CHOICE

1. b **2.** c **3.** d **4.** a **5.** b **6.** a **7.** a **8.** b **9.** d **10.** c

COMPLETION

1. atmosphere **2.** proteins **3.** air pressure **4.** troposphere **5.** Van Allen belts

TRUE OR FALSE

1. T **2.** T **3.** F, decreases **4.** T **5.** F, oxygen

USING SCIENCE SKILLS

1. layer 1, troposphere; layer 2, stratosphere; layer 3, mesosphere; layer 4, ionosphere; layer 5, exosphere; layer 6, thermosphere **2.** tropopause; stratopause **3.** decreases; increases; decreases; increases **4.** stratosphere (2); ionosphere (4)

ESSAY

1. The Van Allen belts are layers of high radiation in the magnetosphere. They contain charged particles. They provide protection for life on the Earth by trapping deadly radiation. **2.** The mesosphere is the third-lowest layer of the atmosphere (ranging between altitudes of 48 km and 80 km). It is the coldest region of the atmosphere, and temperatures decrease within it as altitude increases. When meteoroids enter the mesosphere, they tend to burn up due to friction between them and the atmosphere. **3.** Oxygen is produced by plants during food-making. This process requires carbon dioxide, which the plants remove from the atmosphere. Carbon dioxide is produced by living things during respiration, in which oxygen is removed from the atmosphere and combined with food to release energy. **4.** Additional pollution of the Earth's atmosphere could raise the temperature of the atmosphere. This would cause the polar icecaps to melt, resulting in severe coastal flooding. Additional pollution could limit the amount of radiant energy that reaches the Earth's surface. Another ice age could begin on Earth. Also additional pollution could severely damage people's health. Student suggestions might include burning cleaner fuels, nuclear energy, solar power, electric cars, and geothermal energy.

Name ______________________ Class ____________ Date ____________

Test Bank Test

CHAPTER 1 ■ Earth's Atmosphere

MULTIPLE CHOICE

Write the letter of the answer that best completes each statement.

_____ 1. The Earth's atmosphere contains
- a. minerals.
- b. metamorphic rock.
- c. water.
- d. gases.

_____ 2. We are protected from most of the ultraviolet radiation from the sun because
- a. our atmosphere is rich in ammonia, methane, and water.
- b. ultraviolet radiation first encounters the troposphere as it approaches the Earth.
- c. the water vapor present in the thermosphere blots it out.
- d. ozone absorbs it in the stratosphere.

_____ 3. Our atmosphere contains approximately what percent of oxygen?
- a. 13 percent
- b. 21 percent
- c. 62 percent
- d. 78 percent

_____ 4. What product do green plants give off as waste from their food-making process?
- a. hydrogen
- b. carbon dioxide
- c. oxygen
- d. ozone

_____ 5. All of the following elements are trace gases present in our atmosphere except
- a. xenon.
- b. water vapor.
- c. neon.
- d. helium.

_____ 6. In the nitrogen cycle,
- a. plants release nitrogen as nitrates.
- b. animals release nitrogen directly into the atmosphere.
- c. bacteria combine with other chemicals to make nitrates.
- d. nitrogen gas is used directly by trees to make protein.

_____ 7. During respiration,
- a. carbon dioxide is used directly from the atmosphere.
- b. oxygen is given off as a waste product.
- c. carbon dioxide is joined with food to make free oxygen.
- d. oxygen and food products are combined to release energy.

_____ 8. In comparing the troposphere to the stratosphere, the troposphere
- a. is at the same level as the stratosphere.
- b. touches the Earth while the stratosphere does not.
- c. has a constant temperature of –60°C while the temperature of the stratosphere changes constantly.
- d. contains jet stream winds which are absent in the stratosphere.

_____ **9.** You live in the
a. mesosphere.
b. stratosphere.
c. troposphere.
d. ionosphere.

_____ **10.** The stratopause separates the stratosphere from the
a. mesosphere.
b. troposphere.
c. thermosphere.
d. ionosphere.

_____ **11.** Oxygen is most abundant in the
a. stratosphere.
b. ionosphere.
c. mesosphere.
d. troposphere.

_____ **12.** Satellites that reenter our atmosphere burn up because
a. fuels onboard ignite and set the satellite ablaze.
b. the rubbing of the atmosphere against the satellite causes the satellite to burn.
c. the troposphere is exceedingly hot and causes the satellite to burn.
d. stored energy onboard the satellite is released, causing the satellite to burn.

_____ **13.** The ionosphere is important to communications networks on the Earth because
a. TV stations use the exosphere for transmissions.
b. communications signals pass right through the ionosphere as they pass to outer space.
c. signals bounce off the ionosphere back to Earth.
d. the ionosphere contains vast quantities of helium that strengthen the power of communications signals.

_____ **14.** The coldest region of our atmosphere can be found in the
a. mesosphere.
b. troposphere.
c. thermosphere.
d. stratosphere.

_____ **15.** Living things use nitrogen for
a. breathing.
b. making protein.
c. drinking.
d. making carbohydrates.

_____ **16.** Before the Earth had an ozone layer, the only existing creatures were
a. small reptiles that lived under rocky areas.
b. dinosaurs that thrived in huge swamps.
c. insectlike animals that occupied the upper 10 ft of the ocean waters.
d. microscopic organisms that lived far below the ocean surface.

_____ **17.** The atmosphere gas that is so heavy that it stays near the bottom of the atmosphere is
a. hydrogen.
b. oxygen.
c. helium.
d. ozone.

_____ **18.** From the most abundant to the least abundant, the principal gases in our atmosphere are
a. oxygen, nitrogen, carbon dioxide.
b. carbon dioxide, oxygen, nitrogen.
c. nitrogen, oxygen, carbon dioxide.
d. nitrogen, carbon dioxide, oxygen.

_____ **19.** Oxygen is used by living things to
a. make food.
b. make water.
c. break down water.
d. break down food.

_____ **20.** Water vapor is important in our atmosphere because
a. oxygen combines with it to form protein.
b. it traps heat energy from the sun .
c. it combines with carbon dioxide to form methane.
d. it traps hydrogen in the mesosphere and keeps it from escaping.

_____ **21.** Solid particles are added to the atmosphere by
a. people on the Earth.
b. lightning.
c. rain.
d. the sun.

_____ **22.** As you go higher in the troposphere,
a. the air gets thicker.
b. temperature increases.
c. gases present increase in density.
d. air temperature decreases.

_____ **23.** The reason mountain climbers wear oxygen masks is because
a. high altitude air is rich in ice crystals that they cannot breathe.
b. the air is unclean.
c. the air contains only half as much oxygen at this altitude.
d. at this height, free oxygen in the air freezes.

_____ **24.** The correct order of atmospheric layers from the Earth to outer space is
a. stratosphere, troposphere, mesosphere, thermosphere.
b. troposphere, mesosphere, stratosphere, thermosphere.
c. mesosphere, troposphere, thermosphere, stratosphere.
d. troposphere, stratosphere, mesosphere, thermosphere.

_____ **25.** Ozone is a form of
a. hydrogen.
b. oxygen.
c. nitrogen.
d. carbon dioxide.

_____ **26.** During a rainstorm, large amounts of ozone are released into the atmosphere by
a. bacteria.
b. raindrops.
c. lightning.
d. soil.

_____ **27.** During a storm, you can tell when ozone is present in the air because
a. the sky appears very grey.
b. the air has a burned smell.
c. the clouds have a pink tint.
d. a clean, sharp smell lingers in the air.

_____ **28.** Most of the ultraviolet rays from the sun never reach your skin because
a. convection currents in the stratosphere absorb them.
b. they mix with water vapor in the mesosphere.
c. ozone absorbs them.
d. the jet stream suspends them in the troposphere.

_____ **29.** In our atmosphere, the mesosphere
a. has the warmest temperature of all atmospheric zones.
b. separates the stratosphere from the troposphere.
c. protects us from meteoroids.
d. may reach temperatures as high as 2000°C.

_____ **30.** Our protective Van Allen radiation belts are contained within the
a. ionosphere.
b. thermosphere.
c. stratosphere.
d. magnetosphere.

TRUE OR FALSE

Determine whether each statement is true or false.

_____ **31.** The stratosphere is the entire envelope of gases that surrounds the Earth.

_____ **32.** As the altitude in the atmosphere increases, air becomes colder and less dense.

_____ **33.** Air pressure, caused by gases that surround the Earth, increases as altitude above the Earth increases.

_____ **34.** Nitrogen is less abundant than oxygen in the atmosphere.

_____ **35.** Air pressure is greater in the stratosphere than in the troposphere.

_____ **36.** The troposphere is the layer of the atmosphere nearest the Earth.

_____ **37.** Oxygen is a waste product given off by plants.

_____ **38.** Plants remove carbon dioxide from our atmosphere as they decay.

_____ **39.** James Glaisher discovered the Van Allen belts.

_____ **40.** All of our weather takes place in the troposphere.

COMPLETION

Fill in the word or number that best completes each statement.

______________ **41.** An envelope of gases known as the _____ surrounds the Earth and provides much protection.

______________ **42.** The early atmosphere of the Earth contained the two deadly gases methane and _____.

______________ **43.** The Earth is protected from the severe effects of ultraviolet radiation by a layer of _____ gas present high above its surface.

______________ **44.** The majority of our present-day atmosphere is composed of _____ gas.

______________ **45.** _____ is the one gas necessary for all living things to carry on the process of respiration.

______________ **46.** The process of nitrogen moving from the soil and atmosphere to animals and plants, and then back to the atmosphere and soil, is known as the _____ cycle.

______________ **47.** The layer of gases in our atmosphere is constantly being pushed down toward the Earth because of the pull of _____.

______________ **48.** As warm air rises, streams of air called _____ currents develop and carry much heat into the upper atmosphere.

______________ **49.** The lowest layer of the Earth's atmosphere is called the _____.

______________ **50**. Found at high altitudes, the _____ are strong winds that blow horizontally around the Earth in the lower stratosphere.

______________ **51**. The coldest atmospheric layer is the upper _____.

______________ **52**. Beyond the atmosphere, the _____ is an area around the Earth in which magnetic forces operate.

______________ **53**. Particles given off by the sun and trapped by the Earth's magnetic field collect into bands high above the atmosphere, forming the _____.

______________ **54**. The _____ is that layer of the atmosphere sometimes also known as the "heat sphere," in which temperatures may reach 2000°C.

______________ **55**. Charged particles called _____ are atoms of elements that have either gained or lost electrons.

______________ **56**. The ionosphere is important to the communications industry because _____ bounce off this layer of atmosphere and are reflected back to the Earth's surface.

______________ **57**. Huge disturbances on the sun called _____ are known to increase the concentration of ions present in our ionosphere.

______________ **58**. In the layer of our atmosphere called the _____, the air is extremely thin and any particles present are spread so far apart that they may never hit each other.

______________ **59**. A _____ is a chunk of rocklike matter from outer space.

______________ **60**. Weather satellites orbit the Earth in the upper part of the _____.

USING SCIENCE SKILLS

Use the skills you have developed in the chapter to answer each question.

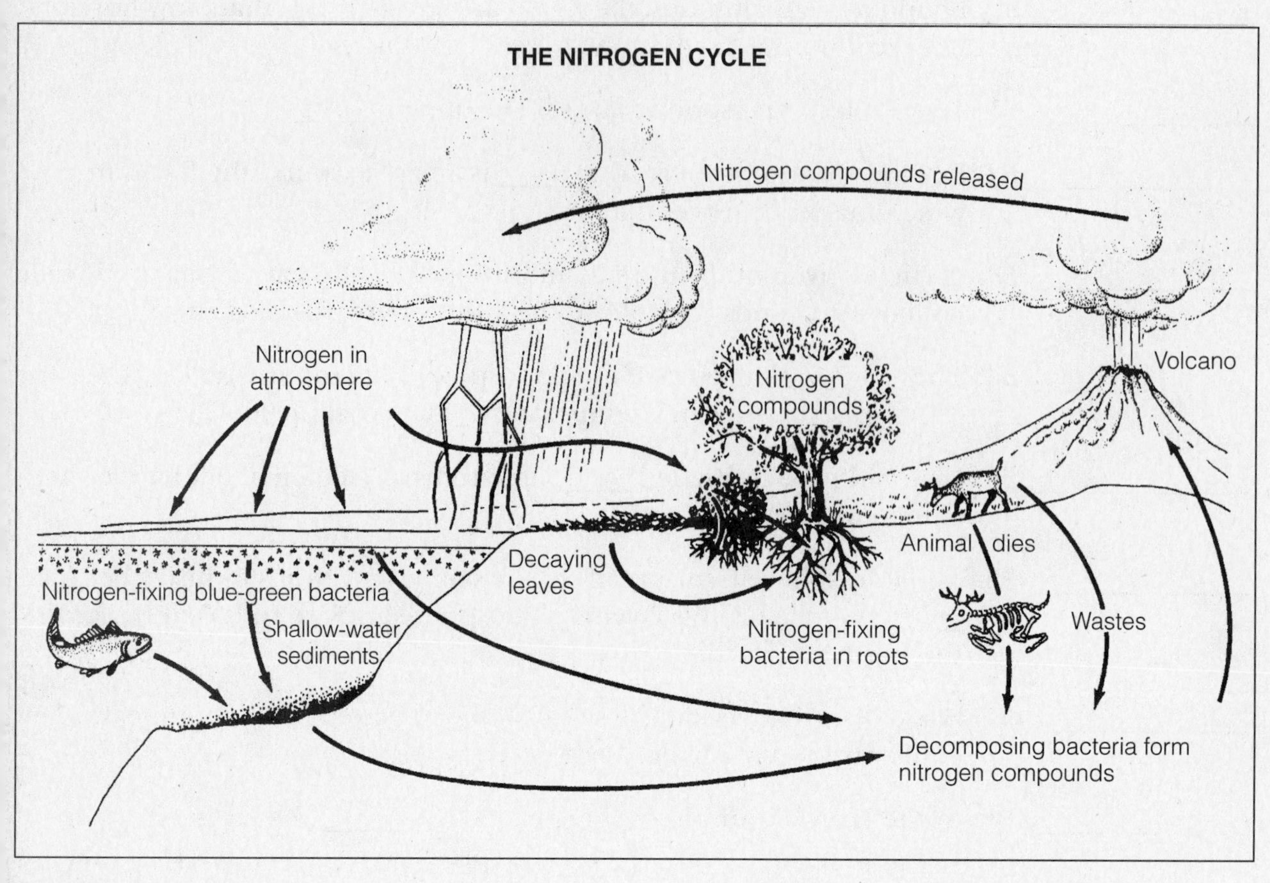

Figure 1

61. In Figure 1, how do land animals contribute nitrogen to the environment?

62. Using Figure 1, explain how nitrogen becomes available to trees.

63. From information given in Figure 1, how can nitrogen be returned from the atmospheric gases to the oceans?

64. How are blue-green bacteria useful in the cycle depicted in Figure 1?

Name ______________________ Class ______________ Date ______________

65. Using the information given in Figure 1, describe the cycle of nitrogen passing from clouds to the flesh of a deer.

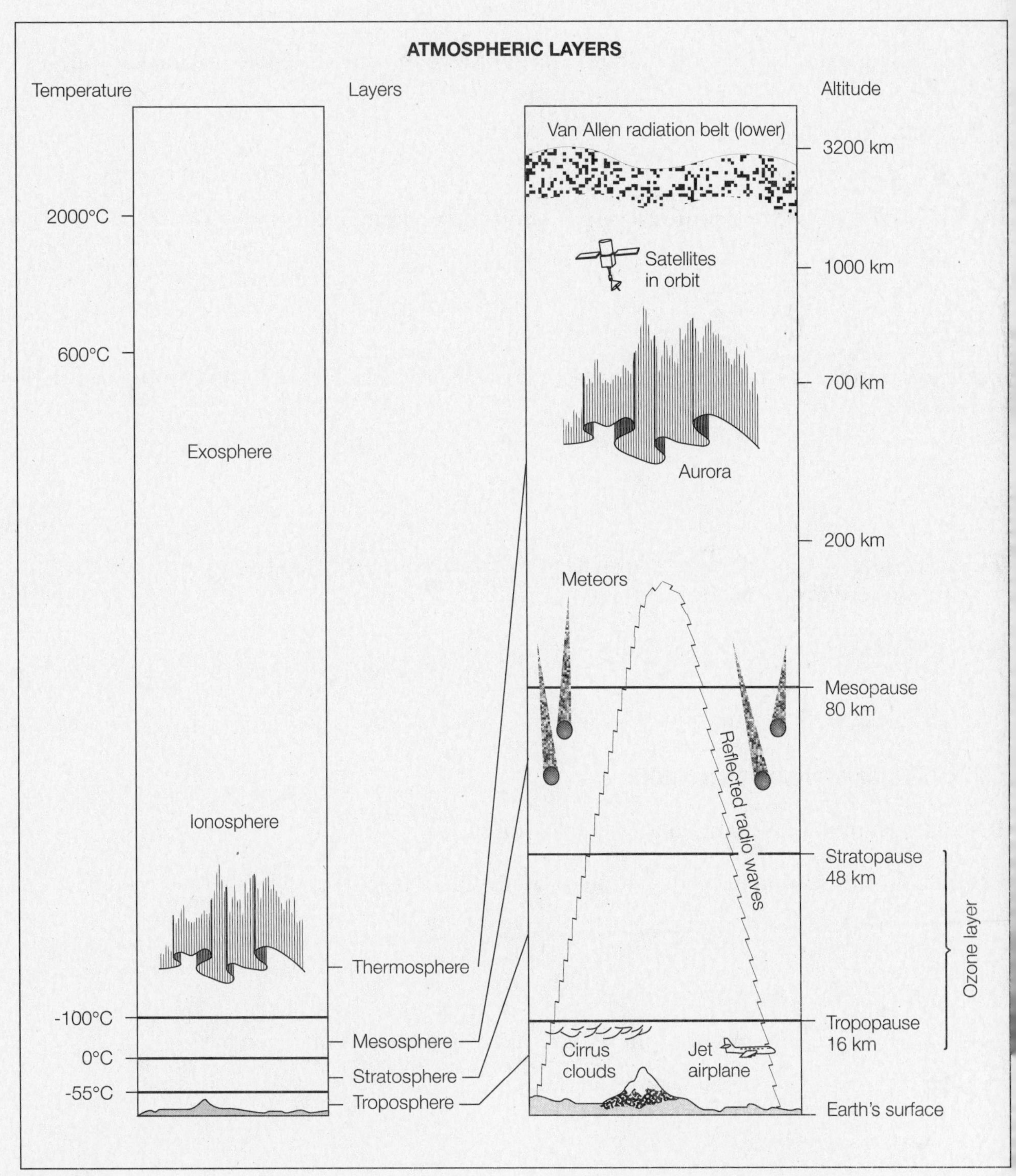

Figure 2

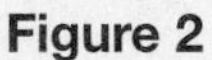

66. According to Figure 2, what is the highest atmospheric temperature?

67. Examine Figure 2. As you go from the Earth through the layers of the atmosphere, what happens to temperature?

68. Using Figure 2, beyond what altitude must one go in order to enter the thermosphere?

69. According to Figure 2, which layers of atmosphere contain the ozone layer?

70. Using Figure 2 as a guide, how many times thicker is the stratosphere than the troposphere?

71. According to Figure 2, what happens to the radio waves sent up from Earth into the atmosphere near an altitude of 200 km?

CRITICAL THINKING AND APPLICATION

Discuss each of the following in a brief paragraph.

72. Explain this statement: "The air in our atmosphere is so strong, it can melt metal."

73. In a 1-L sample of our atmosphere, how many milliliters is nitrogen gas?

74. Design an experiment to prove that air has mass.

75. Explain how the Van Allen belts are both helpful and harmful.

76. Draw a sketch of the Earth's magnetosphere, illustrating the Earth, North and South poles, and lines of force in the magnetosphere.

77. Describe at least two methods of obtaining information about the upper levels of our atmosphere.

78. Do the density and temperature of the atmosphere change as altitude increases through the troposphere and stratosphere? Explain.

79. Describe what ozone is and explain its role in our atmosphere.

80. Explain why mountain climbers need heavy climbing clothing on a high mountain.

81. Explain why pilots must wear oxygen masks at higher altitudes.

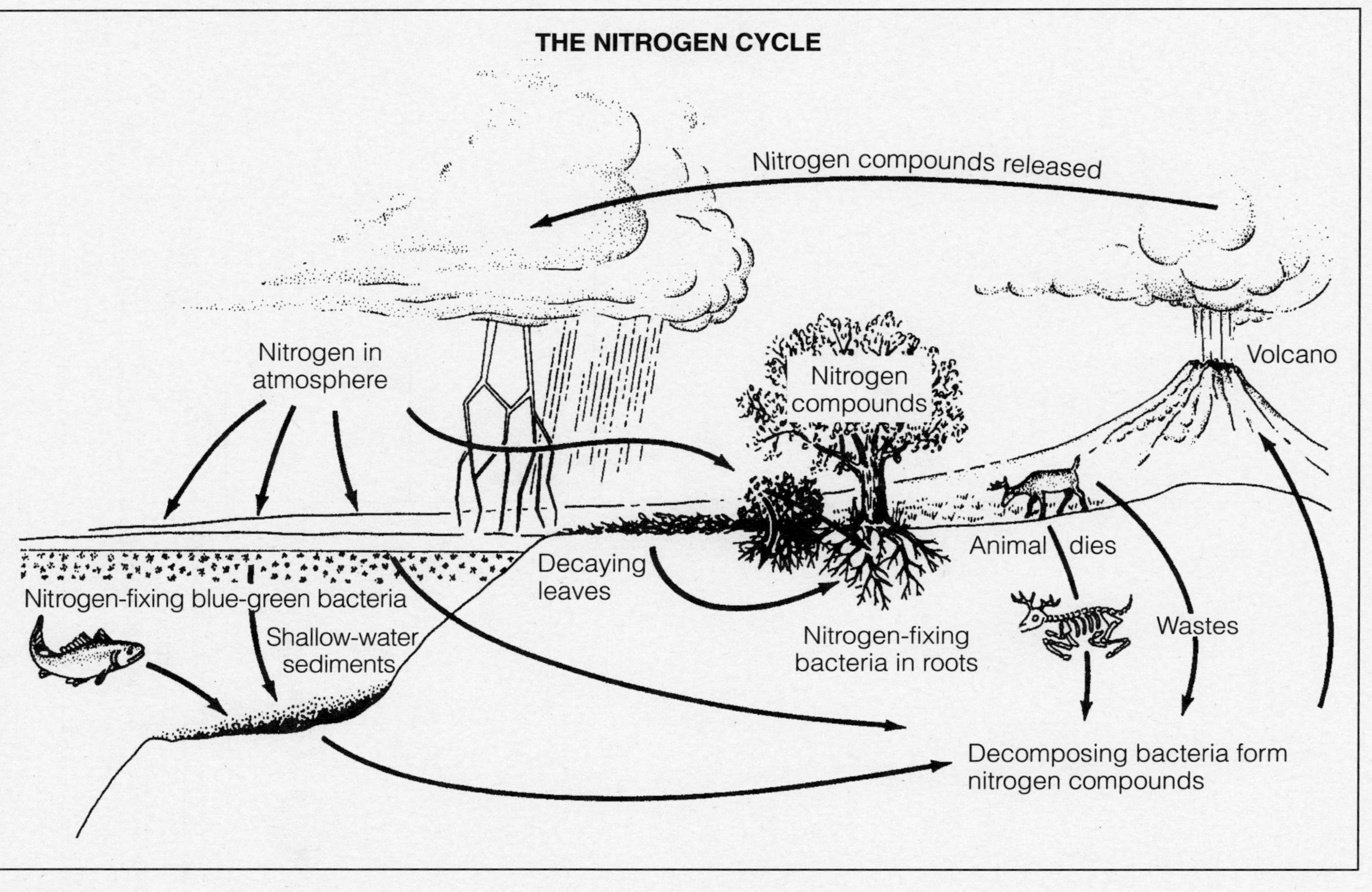
THE NITROGEN CYCLE
Nitrogen compounds released
Nitrogen in atmosphere
Nitrogen compounds
Volcano
Animal dies
Decaying leaves
Nitrogen-fixing blue-green bacteria
Shallow-water sediments
Nitrogen-fixing bacteria in roots
Wastes
Decomposing bacteria form nitrogen compounds

Figure 1

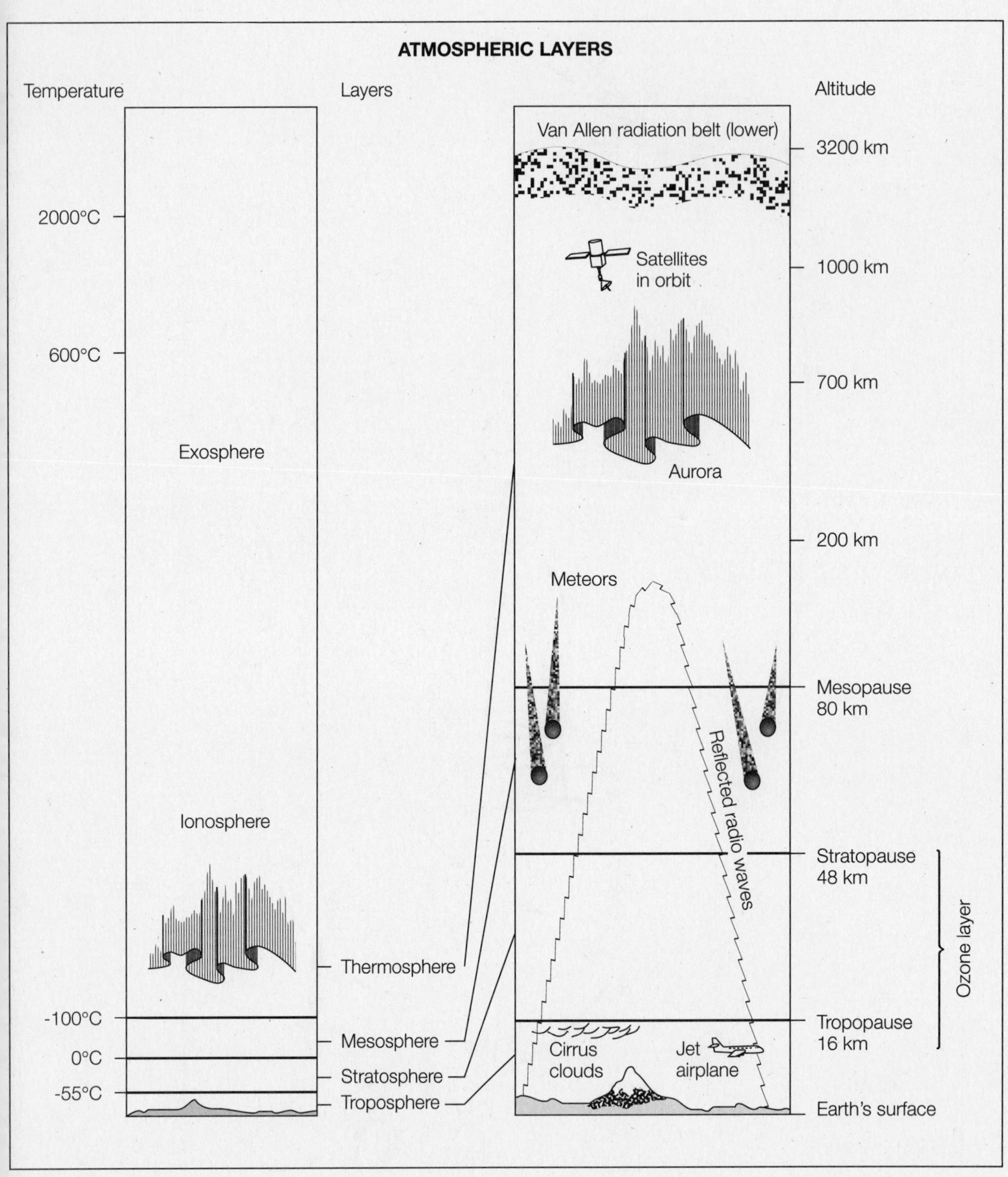
ATMOSPHERIC LAYERS
Temperature
Layers
Altitude
Van Allen radiation belt (lower)
3200 km
2000°C
Satellites
in orbit
1000 km
600°C
700 km
Exosphere
Aurora
200 km
Meteors
Mesopause
80 km
Reflected radio waves
Ionosphere
Stratopause
48 km
Ozone layer
Thermosphere
-100°C
Tropopause
16 km
Mesosphere
Cirrus
clouds
Jet
airplane
0°C
Stratosphere
-55°C
Troposphere
Earth's surface

Figure 2

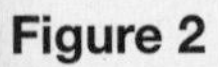

Answer Key

1. c
2. d
3. b
4. c
5. b
6. c
7. d
8. b
9. c
10. b
11. d
12. b
13. c
14. a
15. b
16. d
17. b
18. c
19. d
20. b
21. a
22. d
23. c
24. d
25. b
26. c
27. d
28. c
29. c
30. d
31. F
32. T
33. F
34. F
35. F
36. T
37. T
38. F
39. F
40. F

41. atmosphere
42. ammonia
43. ozone
44. nitrogen
45. oxygen
46. nitrogen
47. gravity
48. convection
49. troposphere
50. jet streams
51. mesosphere
52. magnetosphere
53. Van Allen belts
54. thermosphere
55. ions
56. radio waves
57. solar flares
58. exosphere
59. meteoroid
60. thermosphere
61. Animals return nitrogen to the environment through wastes and through death and decay.
62. Nitrogen in rain and from decaying leaves enters the soil. The nitrogen is taken up by nitrogen-fixing bacteria in tree roots to provide nitrates.
63. Atmospheric nitrogen is returned to the oceans by rainfall.
64. Blue-green bacteria in the aquatic environment combine nitrogen in the water with other elements to make nitrogen usable to plants.
65. The nitrogen in clouds returns to the Earth through rainfall. In the soil the nitrogen bacteria make nitrates. Nitrates are taken up by plants to make protein. The plants are eaten by deer.
66. 2000°C
67. Going from the Earth through the troposphere, the temperature drops at the tropopause, then rises at the stratopause, then drops at the mesopause. As distance increases from the mesopause out into the exosphere, the temperature rises again.
68. 80 km

69. stratosphere and mesosphere
70. 2 times thicker (32 km: 16 km)
71. They are reflected back to the surface of the Earth.
72. As satellites reenter the Earth's atmosphere, the friction of the air rubbing against the metal of the satellite can cause it to melt. A welder's torch uses oxygen in combination with another flammable gas to create extremely high temperatures that melt metal.
73. 1 L = 1000 mL
78% of 1000 mL = .78 x 1000 mL
= 780.00 mL of nitrogen gas
74. Student responses may vary. One approach may be to blow air into two balloons until they are filled. Tie each balloon by a string to the end of a meterstick. Tie a string around the center of the meterstick and use the string to serve as a pivot point to balance the balloons on the opposite ends of the meterstick. Move the string in the center back and forth until the meterstick is exactly level. At this point the masses of the two balloons are equally balanced. Pop one balloon and observe what happens to the other balloon. The second balloon will drop due to the pull of gravity. If any piece of the popped balloon fell to the floor, retie it to the remaining string and popped balloon. Observe that the full balloon still weighs more than the popped balloon.
75. The Van Allen belts are helpful to life on Earth because they trap deadly forms of radiation that would otherwise be harmful. The belts are harmful particularly to space travelers, because the belts emit high levels of dangerous radiation.
76.

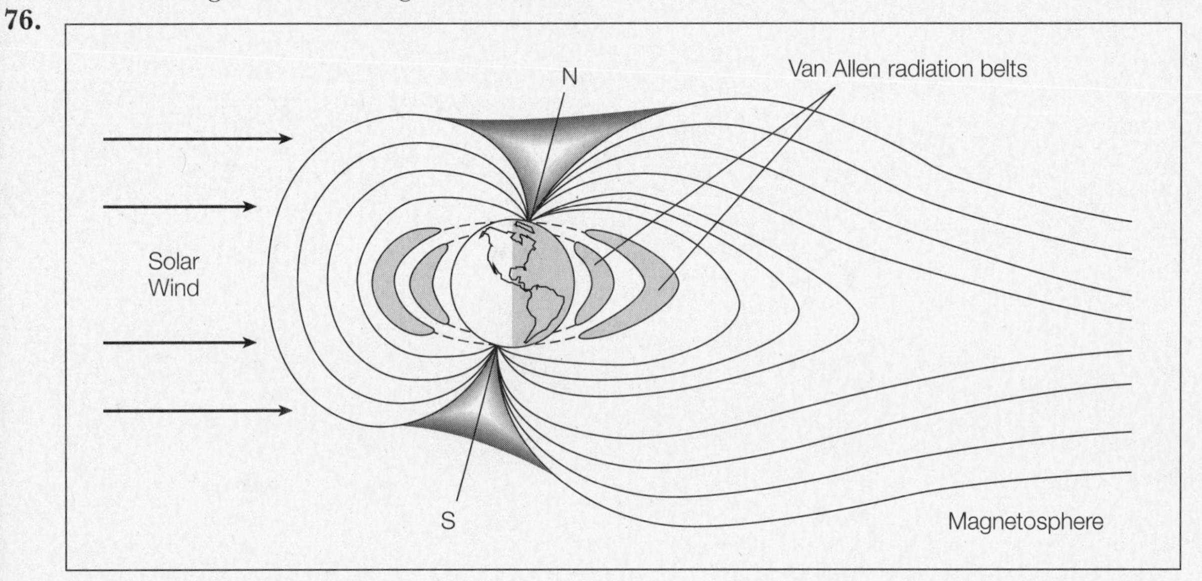

77. Student answers may vary. One method of data gathering is done by satellites in space. Their cameras photograph and transmit pictures back to the Earth for analysis by meteorologists. Other instruments on board collect data about the Earth's atmospheric layers.
A second method of information gathering is by high altitude balloons launched from the Earth that soar to great heights in the upper atmosphere. Instruments attached to the balloons record data about the temperature in the different layers of the atmosphere.
78. The density of the atmosphere decreases with height, and the air gets thinner in the troposphere and stratosphere. The temperature decreases in the troposphere and lower stratosphere. It increases again in the upper stratosphere.
79. Ozone is generated when three atoms of oxygen combine to form one molecule. Ozone forms a layer around the Earth in the upper atmosphere and serves to shield living things against ultraviolet radiation. It also serves as a heat trap, warming the upper stratosphere.
80. Air becomes colder as altitude increases, so mountain climbers need heavy clothing on a high mountain.
81. As altitude increases, air contains less oxygen, so pilots must wear oxygen masks at high altitudes.

Contents

CHAPTER 2 ■ Earth's Oceans

Name ______________________ Class __________ Date __________

Chapter Test

CHAPTER 2 ■ Earth's Oceans

MULTIPLE CHOICE

Write the letter of the correct answer on the line at the left.

_____ **1.** Masses of flowing water that carry sediments down the continental slope are called
a. surface currents.
b. turbidity currents.
c. deep currents.
d. longshore currents.

_____ **2.** Which of the following is not a feature of the ocean floor?
a. abyssal plain
b. trench
c. midocean ridge
d. continental shelf

_____ **3.** A flat-topped seamount is called a(an)
a. guyot.
b. upwelling.
c. midocean ridge.
d. atoll.

_____ **4.** The deepest spot known on the Earth is found in the
a. Mariana Trench.
b. Mid-Atlantic Ridge.
c. Indian Ocean.
d. Mediterranean Sea.

_____ **5.** The percent of the Earth's surface covered by water is approximately
a. 3 percent.
b. 29 percent.
c. 71 percent.
d. 97 percent.

_____ **6.** Ocean temperatures are lowest in the
a. surface zone.
b. deep zone.
c. thermocline.
d. neritic zone.

_____ **7.** Organisms that live on the ocean floor are called
a. benthos.
b. plankton.
c. nekton.
d. swimming organisms.

_____ **8.** The zone between the low- and high-tide lines is called the
a. neritic zone.
b. abyssal zone.
c. bathyal zone.
d. intertidal zone.

_____ **9.** A stream of water that flows parallel to a coast is called a(an)
a. deep current.
b. rip current.
c. longshore current.
d. upwelling.

_____ **10.** Spring tides occur when
a. the moon is in first-quarter phase.
b. the moon is in last-quarter phase.
c. the sun and moon are at right angles to the Earth.
d. the sun and moon are in line with the Earth.

COMPLETION

Complete each statement on the line at the left.

_______________ 1. A scientist who studies the ocean is called a(an) _____.

_______________ 2. A ring of coral reefs surrounding an island that has been worn away and that has sunk beneath the water's surface is called a(an) _____.

_______________ 3. The amount of dissolved salts in ocean water is called _____.

_______________ 4. Organisms that float at or near the ocean's surface are called _____.

_______________ 5. The highest point of a wave is called the _____.

TRUE OR FALSE

Determine whether each statement is true or false. If it is true, write T. If it is false, change the underlined word or words to make the statement true.

_____ _______________ 1. The continental slope and continental shelf together make up the continental rise.

_____ _______________ 2. Midocean ridges are caused by the flow and cooling of molten material from deep within the Earth.

_____ _______________ 3. The Pacific is the world's largest ocean.

_____ _______________ 4. The most abundant salt in ocean water is sodium chloride.

_____ _______________ 5. The most complete picture of the ocean floor was obtained from information gathered by the satellite Challenger.

USING SCIENCE SKILLS: Classifying Objects, Interpreting Illustrations

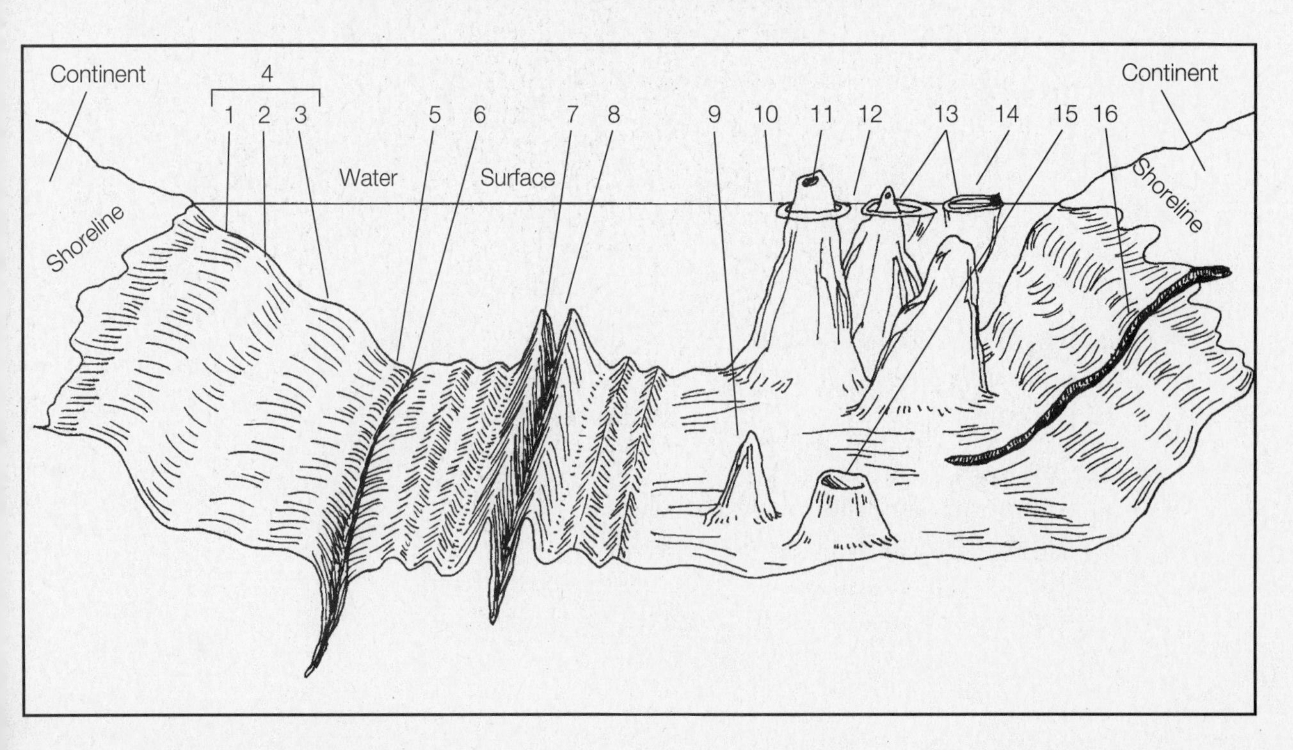

Name ______________________________ Class ______________ Date ____________

1. On the blank line next to each feature below, write the number of the corresponding item in the illustration.

____ a. rift valley

____ b. guyot

____ c. continental slope

____ d. trench

____ e. lagoon

____ f. continental rise

____ g. volcanic island

____ h. submarine canyon

____ i seamount

____ j. continental shelf

____ k. fringing reef

____ l. abyssal plain

____ m. atoll

____ n. midocean ridge

____ o. barrier reef

____ p. continental margin

2. Which features mark the boundary between continental crust and oceanic crust?

____

3. What accounts for the difference between feature 9 and feature 11? ____________

____

Between feature 9 and feature 15? ______________________________

____

4. Which feature is the deepest?______________________________

ESSAY

Write a brief paragraph discussing each of the following statements or questions.

1. Contrast the three kinds of coral reefs.

____

____

____

____

____

2. Describe the location and conditions in the intertidal, neritic, bathyal, and abyssal zones. List one organism that lives in each zone.

3. Describe and account for deep currents and for upwelling. State the practical importance of upwelling.

4. Why might the intertidal zone be hazardous to people who are swimming or boating in the ocean?

Answer Key

MULTIPLE CHOICE

1. b **2.** d **3.** a **4.** a **5.** c **6.** b **7.** a **8.** d **9.** c **10.** d

COMPLETION

1. oceanographer **2.** atoll **3.** salinity **4.** plankton **5.** crest

TRUE OR FALSE

1. F, continental margin **2.** T **3.** T **4.** T **5.** F, Seasat

USING SCIENCE SKILLS

1. a. 7 b. 15 c. 2 d. 5 e. 13 f. 3 g. 11 h. 16 i. 9 j. 1 k. 10 l. 6 m. 14 n. 8 o. 12 p. 4 **2.** the continental slope and continental rise **3.** The seamount (9) and volcanic island (11) are both mountains, but the seamount is not high enough to rise above the water surface. The seamount differs from the guyot (15) in that the former rises to a peak and the latter has a flat top caused by wave erosion. **4.** The trench (5) is deepest.

ESSAY

1. A fringing reef touches the shoreline of a volcanic island. A barrier reef is separated from the island it surrounds by a lagoon; the island has generally sunk downward but has not been completely submerged. An atoll forms a ring around a lagoon; the island it surrounded has worn away and sunk beneath the water's surface. **2.** The intertidal zone lies between low- and high-tide lines and is subject to tidal and wave motion. Crabs, clams, anemones, mussels, seaweed, and marine worms are examples of organisms living there. The neritic zone extends from the low-tide line to the end of a continental shelf, extends to a depth of about 280 m, and has plenty of sunlight, fairly constant temperature, and low water pressure. Fish, clams, snails, whales, and lobsters are examples of organisms living there. The bathyl zone (the less deep of the two open-ocean zones) begins at the continental slope, extends down about 2000 m, and is not lit to the bottom by sunlight. Organisms include squid, octopus, and large whales. The abyssal zone (the deeper open-ocean zone) begins at a depth of about 2000 m, extends down to the ocean floor, is not penetrated by sunlight, and is subject to very high water pressure and low temperatures. Organisms include the anoplogaster, devilfish, and anglerfish. **3.** Deep currents are streaming motions of water far below the surface. They are caused by water density differences, and generally involve the flow of colder, saltier, denser water from polar regions under warm, less dense water. Upwelling is the rising of deep cold currents to the ocean surface and is due to the rising of the ocean floor near the land. The rising currents carry with them rich foodstuffs from the ocean floor that support a great deal of ocean life, making for high availability of fish for human consumption. **4.** Swimmers and small boats would be in danger of being pulled out away from shore during low tide. It is also possible that if high tide came in very quickly, swimmers or small boats could be overwhelmed by water. In addition, the breaking of waves could be very hard on boats, and a large wave might overwhelm a swimmer.

Name ______________________ Class ______________ Date ____________

Test Bank Test

CHAPTER 2 ■ Earth's Oceans

MULTIPLE CHOICE

Write the letter of the answer that best completes each statement.

_____ **1**. The largest ocean in the world is the
a. Atlantic. c. Mediterranean.
b. Pacific. d. Indian.

_____ **2**. Ocean water differs from lake water in that it has
a. animal life. c. salt.
b. sediment. d. plant life.

_____ **3**. The heat from the sun's rays causes ocean water to
a. condense. c. precipitate.
b. extrude. d. evaporate.

_____ **4**. As ocean water leaves the ocean and becomes a part of the atmosphere, it change from a
a. liquid to a solid. c. vapor to a liquid.
b. solid to a vapor. d. liquid to a vapor.

_____ **5**. What percent of the Earth's crust is covered by ocean water?
a. 97 percent. c. 50 percent.
b. 61 percent. d. 71 percent.

_____ **6**. A part of an ocean that is nearly surrounded by land is a(an)
a. canyon. c. sea.
b. island. d. river.

_____ **7**. The deepest ocean in the world is the
a. Arctic Ocean. c. Indian Ocean.
b. Pacific Ocean. d. Atlantic Ocean.

_____ **8**. An ocean is different from a sea because
a. the water in an ocean is salty and sea water is not.
b. animals in the sea are completely different.
c. seas are smaller than oceans.
d. oceans are located higher than seas.

_____ **9**. When testing ocean water for salinity, you will express the amount of salts present in units called
a. meters per liter. c. parts per thousand.
b. kilograms per centimeter. d. grams per millimeter.

_____ **10**. One kilogram of sea water that contains 25 g of dissolved salts should contain how much pure water?
a. 65 g c. 85 g
b. 850 g d. 965 g

_____ **11.** In the oceans of the world, sodium chloride is
a. less abundant than magnesium chloride.
b. more abundant than water.
c. more abundant than magnesium sulfate.
d. less abundant than calcium carbonate.

_____ **12.** The salts present in the oceans do not come from
a. the action of waves along shorelines.
b. rains that fall into the oceans.
c. volcanoes erupting in the oceans.
d. major rivers eroding inland areas.

_____ **13.** Evaporation of ocean water will cause
a. the salinity of oceans to decrease.
b. oceans to get considerably cooler.
c. salts present to become more concentrated.
d. the volume of ocean water to increase.

_____ **14.** At a point where the Mississippi River empties into the Gulf of Mexico, the salinity of the water would be
a. higher than the open gulf water.
b. lower than the river water.
c. the same as the open gulf water.
d. lower than the open gulf water.

_____ **15.** In warm oceans where there is little rainfall,
a. the content of dissolved salts is high.
b. animal life is nonexistent.
c. the salinity of the water is low.
d. dissolved salts are absent.

_____ **16.** The temperature of ocean water is highest
a. in the deep ocean zone.
b. in the zone of the thermocline.
c. at the bottom.
d. on the surface.

_____ **17.** Most oceans have a thermocline because
a. the temperature of the deep zone exceeds that of the thermocline.
b. heat from deep ocean vents provides heat for the thermocline.
c. layers of ocean water do not mix easily.
d. the surface zone has a very high salinity.

_____ **18.** The surface zone, thermocline, and deep zones are not found in the
a. Atlantic Ocean.
b. Arctic Ocean.
c. Indian Ocean.
d. Pacific Ocean.

_____ **19.** As you descend through the thermocline, you will
a. encounter a region of high sunlight.
b. measure no temperature change.
c. see areas rich in plant life.
d. experience a drastic drop in temperature.

_____ **20.** When compared to cold water, warm ocean water
a. holds less dissolved gases.
b. contains the same amount of dissolved gases.
c. sinks because it is heavier.
d. can hold more oxygen.

_____ **21.** After having studied the features of seamounts present in the oceans, you can conclude that they are
a. found only on the continental slope.
b. of volcanic origin.
c. the remains of eroded continents.
d. ordinary shoreline features that are found in the Atlantic Ocean.

_____ **22.** When leaving the shore and going out to sea, you would first pass over the
a. continental rise.
b. abyssal plain.
c. continental slope.
d. continental shelf.

_____ **23.** Ocean creatures who are able to make their own food are
a. plankton.
b. coral.
c. nekton.
d. crabs.

_____ **24.** The height of a wave is the
a. distance between the still water level and the crest.
b. distance between two successive troughs.
c. distance between the trough and the crest.
d. distance between the trough and the still water level.

_____ **25.** The height of a surface wave is not dependent on
a. length of time the wind blows across the water.
b. the salinity of the water.
c. the wind speed.
d. the distance the wind blows over the water.

_____ **26.** Deep currents are caused mainly by
a. different water densities.
b. the up and down movement of sea water.
c. the spinning of the Earth.
d. warm water moving over cold water.

_____ **27.** A large flat area on the ocean floor is called a(an)
a. abyssal plain.
b. guyot.
c. continental shelf.
d. atoll.

_____ **28.** A long narrow crevice that can be more than 11,000 m deep is called a
a. midocean ridge.
b. guyot.
c. submarine canyon.
d. trench.

_____ **29.** A ring of coral reefs surrounding an island that has sunk beneath the water's surface is called a(an)
a. atoll.
b. barrier reef.
c. fringing reef.
d. guyot.

_____ 30. Giant waves caused by earthquakes are called
a. upwellings.
b. crests.
c. tsunamis.
d. tides.

TRUE OR FALSE

Determine whether each statement is true or false.

_____ 31. The two most abundant elements that make up ocean water are oxygen and nitrogen.

_____ 32. Animals that live in the ocean need oxygen to live.

_____ 33. Ocean fishing areas are found in the waters located over the continental slope.

_____ 34. Small sea creatures that depend entirely on floating and drifting in the oceans are the nekton.

_____ 35. Thermoclines occur at a specific depth in the ocean.

_____ 36. The crest is the highest point on an ocean wave.

_____ 37. Atolls are long, rounded waves that are commonly found far out at sea.

_____ 38. To prevent being washed out to sea, intertidal animals attach themselves to sand or rocks in the area.

_____ 39. About 97 percent of the Earth's water is ocean water.

_____ 40. The abyssal zone of the ocean is considered to be a deeper zone than the bathyl zone.

COMPLETION

Fill in the word or number that best completes each statement.

______________ 41. The ocean is studied by scientists called _____.

______________ 42. In ocean water, _____ is the number of grams of salt present in 1 kg of water.

______________ 43. The major water bodies of the world are the _____, Indian, and _____ oceans.

______________ 44. Two gases dissolved in ocean water that are vital to living things are _____ and _____.

______________ 45. Large, flat areas known as _____ cover vast regions of the ocean floor.

______________ 46. Underwater volcanic mountains called _____ rise above the surrounding ocean floor and are very numerous in the Pacific Ocean.

______________ 47. A(An) _____ is an enormous, narrow crevice or crack in the ocean floor that can exceed 10,000 m in depth.

______________ 48. Rift valleys in the ocean are marked by many volcanic eruptions and _____ that cause the Earth to tremble.

______________ **49**. Unusual looking islands in the ocean known as _____ develop on volcanoes and form from the remains of sea animals.

______________ **50**. Very small organisms called _____ live in the oceans by drifting with the currents of water, and serve as food for many of the larger animals in the sea.

______________ **51**. Able to get food and fight off predators, _____ can swim and move from area to area in the oceans.

______________ **52**. Flat-topped seamounts known as _____ do not rise to the surface of the ocean.

______________ **53**. As a group, creatures that crawl over or are attached to the bottom of the ocean floor are called _____.

______________ **54**. Because it is the most changeable zone in the ocean, the _____ zone is a severe environment for living creatures to exist.

______________ **55**. The _____ zone of the ocean is rich in sunlight, extends some 200 m down from the surface, and is a home for whales and fish.

______________ **56**. The horizontal distance from one trough to the next consecutive trough in the same wave is referred to as the _____.

______________ **57**. An earthquake-generated _____ is a massive wave of long wavelength and becomes the largest wave found in the ocean.

______________ **58**. The _____ is an example of a wind-driven surface current that carries water around the tip of Florida and on past the eastern seaboard of the United States.

______________ **59**. A(An) _____ is the periodic rise and fall of ocean water due to the pull of gravity of the sun and moon on the oceans of the Earth.

______________ **60**. The process of _____ brings deep, cold currents of water up to the surface of the ocean.

USING SCIENCE SKILLS

Use the skills you have developed in the chapter to answer each question.

Tides for a particular coastline are predicted based on records of tides that have occurred in the area for many years. The data below show the tides predicted for 3 days at Baffin Bay.

Baffin Bay Tide Data Table

Day	Time	Height (meters)
Monday	6:00 AM	1.5
	2:00 PM	6.7
	10:30 PM	1.7
Tuesday	7:30 AM	6.5
	5:00 PM	1.9
	3:00 AM	6.3
Wednesday	1:30 PM	2.1
	12:30 AM	6.1
	12:30 PM	2.3
	12:00 AM	5.9

Figure 3

61. Using the data given in Figure 3, plot the tide heights on the graph in Figure 4.

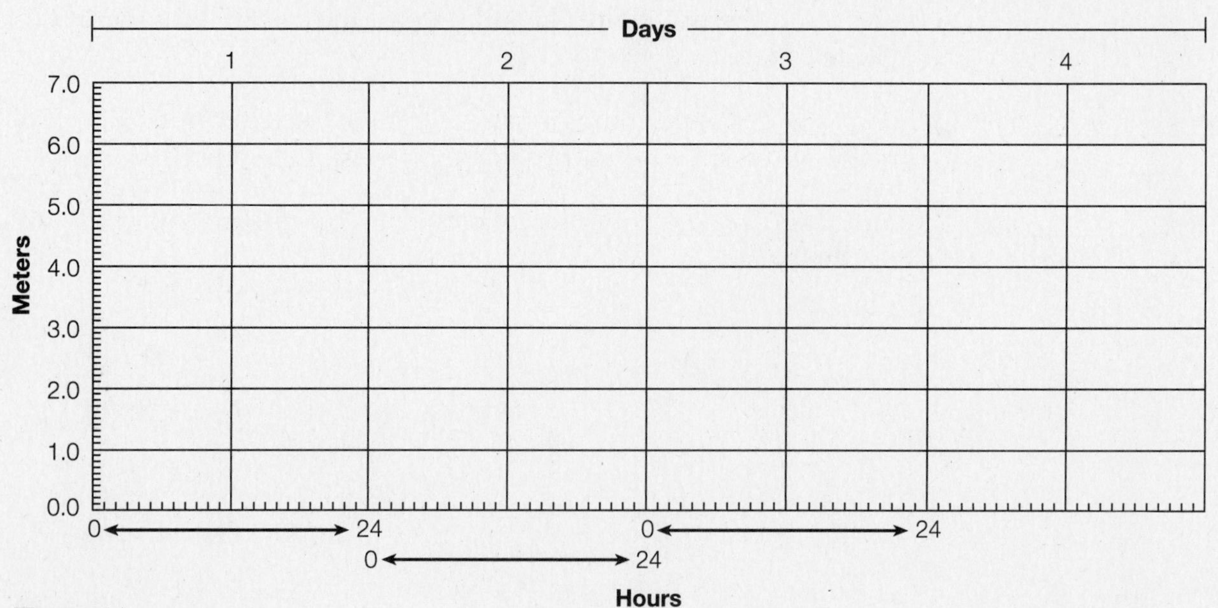

Figure 4

Name ______________________ Class ______________ Date ____________

62. Using the data in Figure 3, how many tides will occur on Monday? How many low tides? High tides?

63. Using the data in Figure 3, predict the height of the next low tide that will occur after the 5.9 m tide.

64. Based on the data in Figure 3, make a general statement about what the tides will do over the period of 3 days.

65. Using the data in Figure 3, how much difference is there in height between low tide and high tide on Wednesday?

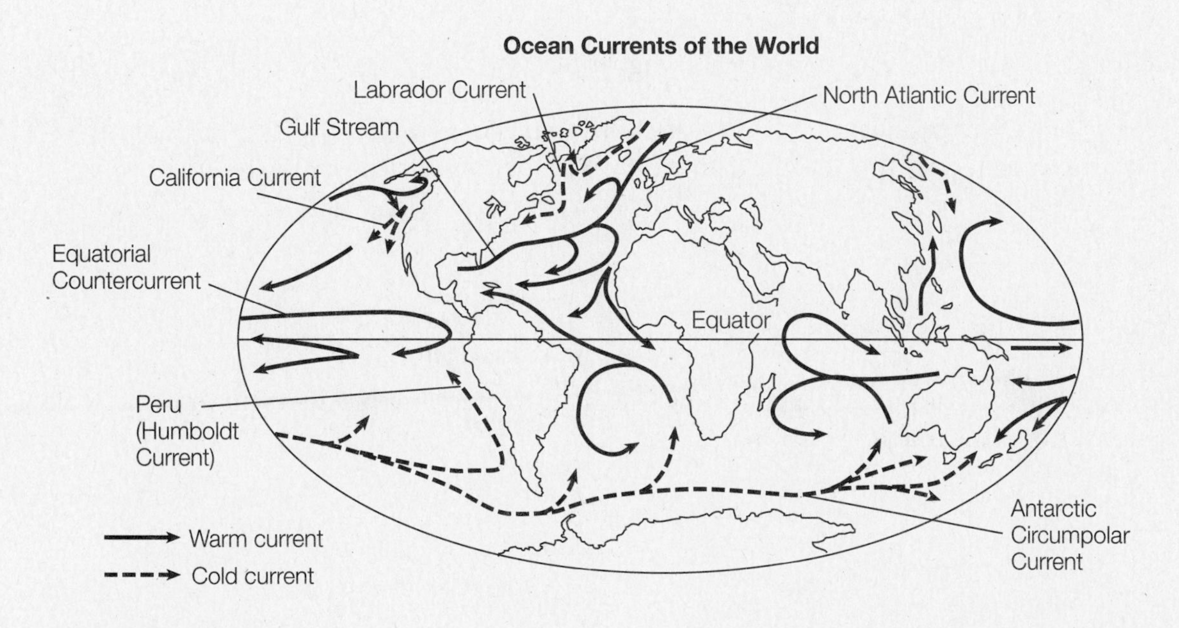

Figure 5

66. In which direction does the equatorial countercurrent flow in Figure 5?

67. Why does the Humboldt Current flow northward in the Pacific Ocean, as shown in Figure 5?

68. Which currents in Figure 5 flow along the coastlines of the United States?

69. Using Figure 5, describe what type of currents are found at the equator and in which direction they flow.

70. Using Figure 5, make a general statement about the circulation of currents in the Indian Ocean.

CRITICAL THINKING AND APPLICATION

Discuss each of the following in a brief paragraph.

71. As you sit on the beach, you watch a stick bob up and down in the surf and count a total of 21 waves that pass the stick in 1 minute. What is the frequency of the incoming waves?

72. Explain with the aid of a diagram how swells at sea become breakers and crash on the beach when they reach the shore.

73. Discuss at least three ways in which oceans are useful to people.

74. Explain where waves get their energy.

75. How would the climate of the western European coastline change if the Gulf Stream ceased to flow across the Atlantic Ocean to Europe?

76. Design an experiment to test the hypothesis that the densest water in the ocean comes from the cold Arctic and Antarctic. Test only one variable in your experiment.

77. Sea water with a salinity of 35 parts per thousand contains 27.2 parts per thousand sodium chloride. How much salt will 100 kg of this sea water produce?

78. Compare the movement of surface currents with the movement of deep currents.

79. Oceanographers sent sonar waves down to the bottom of the Atlantic Ocean to determine how deep a trench was. It took the sonar waves 14 seconds to go down and come back up to the ship. Scientists know that sound travels 1500 m per second in sea water. How deep is the trench beneath the ship?

80. Compare the plankton and nekton of the oceans. How are they alike and how are they different?

Baffin Bay Tide Data Table		
Day	**Time**	**Height (meters)**
Monday	6:00 AM	1.5
	2:00 PM	6.7
	10:30 PM	1.7
Tuesday	7:30 AM	6.5
	5:00 PM	1.9
	3:00 AM	6.3
Wednesday	1:30 PM	2.1
	12:30 AM	6.1
	12:30 PM	2.3
	12:00 AM	5.9

Figure 3

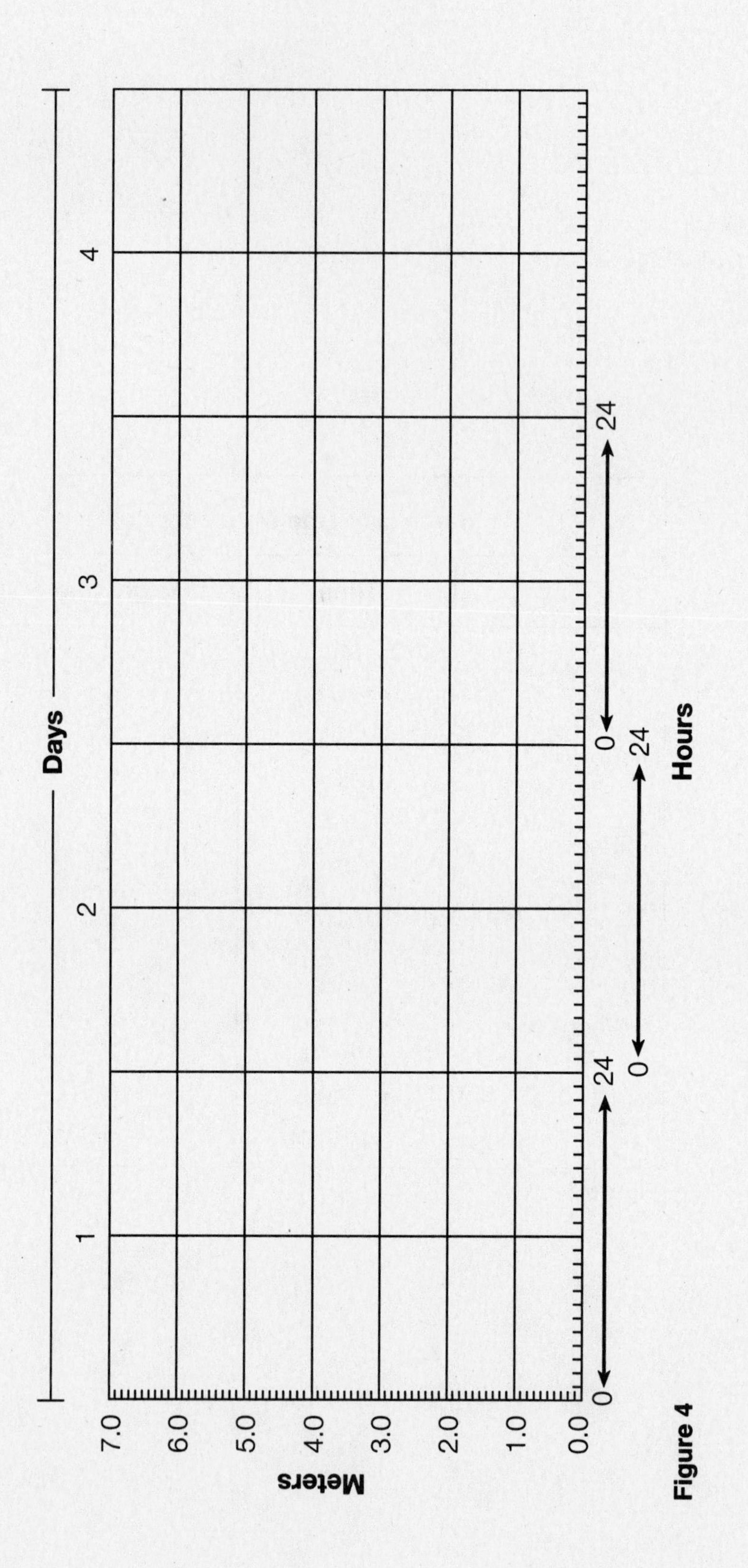

Figure 4

Ocean Currents of the World

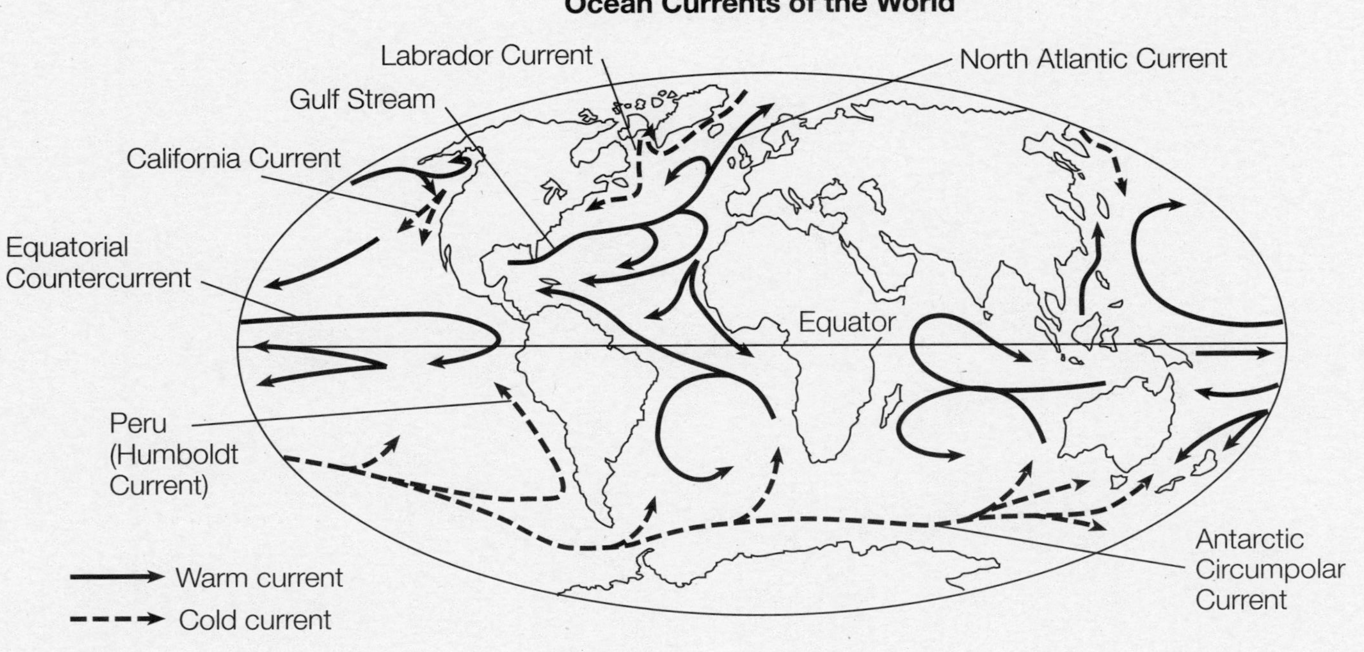

Figure 5

Answer Key

1. b
2. c
3. d
4. d
5. d
6. c
7. b
8. c
9. c
10. d
11. c
12. b
13. c
14. d
15. a
16. d
17. c
18. b
19. d
20. a
21. b
22. d
23. a
24. c
25. b
26. a
27. a
28. d
29. a
30. c
31. F
32. T
33. F
34. F
35. F
36. T
37. F
38. T
39. T
40. T

41. oceanographers
42. salinity
43. Pacific, Atlantic
44. oxygen, carbon dioxide
45. abyssal plaints
46. seamounts
47. trench
48. earthquakes
49. coral reefs
50. plankton
51. nekton
52. guyots
53. benthos
54. intertidal
55. neritic
56. wavelength
57. tsunami
58. Gulf Stream
59. tide
60. upwelling
61. Check student graphs.
62. 3, 2, 1
63. 2.5 m
64. High tides get lower and low tides get higher.
65. 4.2 m
66. West to east
67. The western coastline of South America runs north and south, causing the Humboldt Current to flow parallel with the coastline.
68. Gulf Stream, Labrador Current, California Current
69. Currents at the equator are warm and all seem to flow somewhat parallel to the equator until they come in contact with a continental landmass.
70. The major currents in the Indian Ocean are warm currents that move from east to west until they contact the east coast of Africa. There they split and move in a circular pattern northward and southward.

71. frequency = $\frac{\text{number of waves}}{\text{time}} = \frac{\text{21 waves}}{\text{60 seconds}}$ = .35 waves per second
72. As swells near the shore, they slow down. Their wavelengths decrease and their heights increase because they come into shallow water. They finally crash over as breakers on the shore.
73. Student answers may vary. Oceans provide food through fishing and aquaculture or seafarming. The oceans also serve as important shipping lanes for cargo and petroleum products. Ocean water provides salt for regions of the world where it is much needed and provides many elements that are extracted and used by people.
74. Waves get their energy from winds, earthquakes, and the gravitational attraction of the moon. As wind transfers energy to the water, waves grow with the energy passing through the water. The water remains relatively still and undisturbed.
75. The Gulf Stream brings warm waters to the European coast, causing moderate climate conditions along the coast. If this process stopped, the climate of the region would turn colder.
76. Student responses may vary, but all experiments should show that the density of cold water is greater than that of warm water. One experiment might be to take two narrow-mouth bottles, fill one with cold water colored blue, and the other with warm water colored red. Allow water from both bottles to mingle. As time lapses, the blue water will pass under the red water because it is more dense than the red water. In this experiment, only the temperature was changed. The color was added to make the two water types distinguishable.
77. 1 kg sea water = 27.2 g salt
    100 kg sea water = 27.2 g × 100
    = 2720 g salt
78. Both currents exhibit movement. However, surface currents are caused by the winds against the surface of the water, while deep currents are set in motion by big differences in water density. The colder the water is, the more dense and heavier it is; thus, it will move more quickly than less cold water.
79. depth = speed of sound in water × time it takes to travel to the bottom. Since the total trip took 14 seconds, the time to the bottom is only 7 seconds.
    depth = 1500 m/sec × 7 sec
    = 10,500 m to the bottom.
80. Nekton and plankton both live in ocean water, and both need energy and nutrients to live. Nekton differs from plankton in that these creatures are able to move around by their own power and search for food. Plankton cannot swim under their own power and must depend on the currents to carry them from location to location.

Contents

CHAPTER 3 ■ Earth's Fresh Water

Name ______________________________ Class ______________ Date ______________

Chapter Test

CHAPTER 3 ■ Earth's Fresh Water

MULTIPLE CHOICE

Write the letter of the correct answer on the line at the left.

_____ **1.** During condensation,
a. vapor turns to liquid.
b. liquid turns to vapor.
c. liquid turns to solid.
d. liquid falls to the Earth as rain or snow.

_____ **2.** Crevasses are
a. caverns.
b. glaciers.
c. cracks on the surface of glaciers.
d. stalactites.

_____ **3.** Meltwater is a stream of water formed by
a. melting snow.
b. surface runoff from ice.
c. an iceberg.
d. a valley glacier.

_____ **4.** Large chunks of ice that break off from glaciers and drift into the sea are called
a. continental glaciers.
b. icebergs.
c. aquifers.
d. stalagmites.

_____ **5.** A land area in which surface runoff drains into a system of rivers is called a(an)
a. aquifer.
b. watershed.
c. zone of aeration.
d. zone of saturation.

_____ **6.** The main difference between a pond and a lake is the
a. amount of salt in the water.
b. purity of the water.
c. depth of the water.
d. temperature of the water.

_____ **7.** An artificial body of fresh water often used as a source of drinking water is called a(an)
a. aquifer.
b. reservoir.
c. water table.
d. watershed.

_____ **8.** Clay and other materials through which water cannot readily pass are said to be
a. permeable.
b. impermeable.
c. polar.
d. hard.

_____ **9.** A drilled water source from which water flows upward without being pumped is called a(an)
a. artesian well.
b. aquifer.
c. water table.
d. water cycle.

_____ **10.** The polarity of water is due to
a. the charged ends of its molecules.
b. the presence of minerals.
c. its purity.
d. its hardness.

COMPLETION

Complete each statement on the line at the left.

_______________ 1. The continuous movement of water from oceans and fresh water to air and land and back to oceans is called the _____.

_______________ 2. Water that remains in the ground is called _____.

_______________ 3. A large mass of moving ice and snow is called a(an) _____.

_______________ 4. A layer of rock or sediment through which water can move freely is called a(an) _____.

_______________ 5. The surface between the zone of aeration and the zone of saturation is called the _____.

TRUE OR FALSE

Determine whether each statement is true or false. If it is true, write T. If it is false, change the underlined word or words to make the statement true.

_____ _______________ 1. Fresh water makes up a small percentage of the Earth's water.

_____ _______________ 2. The process in which water returns to the Earth as rain or snow is called sublimation.

_____ _______________ 3. The space between particles of soil is called the pore space.

_____ _______________ 4. There is less fresh water below the surface of the land than there is in all the lakes and reservoirs on the Earth's surface.

_____ _______________ 5. Water that does not contain dissolved minerals is called soft water.

USING SCIENCE SKILLS: Applying Concepts, Interpreting Diagrams

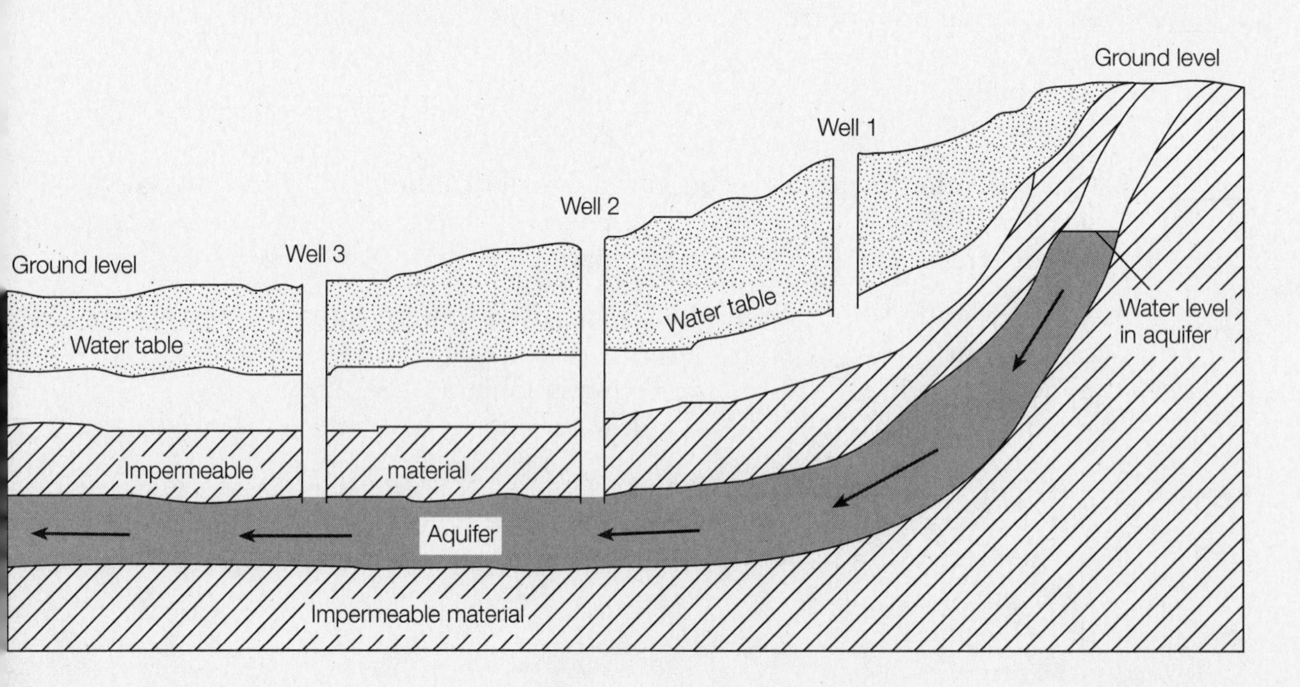

Name ______________________ Class ____________ Date ____________

1. What is a zone of aeration? ______________________
Label this zone on the diagram.

2. What is a zone of saturation? ______________________
Label this zone on the diagram.

3. To what level can water in Well 1 rise on its own? ______________________

In Well 2? ______________________

In Well 3? ______________________
Label these on the diagram.

4. What is an artesian well? ______________________

____

Which, if any, of the wells are artesian? ______________________

ESSAY

Write a brief paragraph discussing each of the following statements.

1. Explain the water cycle and the processes involved in it.

____

____

____

____

____

____

____

____

2. Contrast valley glaciers and continental glaciers.

____

____

____

____

____

____

3. Explain the nature and function of a watershed.

4. Describe the formation of underground caverns, stalactites, and stalagmites.

5. Explain the dissolving of salt by water. Include the terms *molecule, polar, ion, solvent,* and *solution* in your answer.

MULTIPLE CHOICE

1. a **2.** c **3.** d **4.** b **5.** b **6.** c **7.** b **8.** b **9.** a **10.** a

COMPLETION

1. water cycle **2.** groundwater **3.** glacier **4.** aquifer **5.** water table

TRUE OR FALSE

1. T **2.** F, precipitation **3.** T **4.** F, more **5.** T

USING SCIENCE SKILLS

1. A region in which soil pore spaces are filled mostly with air. Check student diagrams. **2.** A region in which the pores are filled with water. Check student diagrams. **3.** Up to the water table. Up to the water level in the aquifer. Up to the water level in the aquifer. Check student diagrams. **4.** A well from which water flows without pumping; Wells 2 and 3.

ESSAY

1. The water cycle is a continuous movement of water. Liquid water on the Earth's surface evaporates, or changes to vapor, by absorbing the energy of the sun. When air containing the vapor cools, the vapor condenses, or changes back to a liquid. The water then falls to the Earth as rain, snow, sleet, or hail, in the precipitation process. Then the evaporation stage occurs again. **2.** A valley glacier is long and narrow and moves downhill between the steep sides of a mountain valley. A continental glacier occurs in the polar region, where thick sheets of snow and ice build up and move outward in all directions. It can cover millions of square kilometers of the Earth's surface. **3.** Watersheds are land areas in which surface runoff drains into a river or system of rivers and streams. Watersheds prevent floods and water shortages by controlling water flow into streams and rivers, and provide a steady flow of fresh water into oceans. The fresh water from watersheds is used for drinking, irrigation, and other purposes. **4.** As water moves down through soil, it combines with carbon dioxide to form a weak acid that can dissolve underlying limestone. Groundwater enters and widens cracks in the limestone. Eventually, large underground passages and caverns can form. Stalactites hang down from the cavern ceilings, and stalagmites rise up from the floors. These iciclelike formations develop from dissolved substances in groundwater. **5.** Water molecules are polar, or have oppositely charged ends. They attract ions, or charged particles, that make up the salt. The ions are "pulled" out of the solid by the solvent water, producing a solution, or mixture on the molecular level.

Name ______________________ Class ______________ Date __________

Test Bank Test

CHAPTER 3 ■ Earth's Fresh Water

MULTIPLE CHOICE

Write the letter of the answer that best completes each statement.

_____ **1.** Ocean water cannot be used for living things because it
a. contains sediments.
b. is too warm.
c. contains oxygen.
d. contains salt.

_____ **2.** Most of the fresh water on Earth is not usable because it is
a. polluted.
b. in the oceans.
c. frozen in ice.
d. permanently stored in clouds.

_____ **3.** We do not run out of fresh water because
a. the rock cycle renews it.
b. renewed amounts come from processing plants.
c. evaporation fills lakes.
d. the hydrologic cycle renews it.

_____ **4.** Of all the water on Earth, fresh water makes up approximately
a. 2 percent.
b. 3 percent.
c. 5 percent.
d. 10 percent.

_____ **5.** Evaporation in nature occurs because
a. water has the ability to turn into ice.
b. artesian wells flow freely.
c. water is heated by the sun.
d. cool air comes into contact with cool water.

_____ **6.** Some water returns to the atmosphere through
a. plasticity.
b. evaporation.
c. precipitation.
d. condensation.

_____ **7.** All of the following are forms of precipitation except
a. snow.
b. hail.
c. water vapor.
d. rain.

_____ **8.** In the process of condensation,
a. water changes to ice.
b. water vapor becomes liquid water
c. liquid water changes to water vapor.
d. ice changes to water vapor.

_____ **9.** Scientists are studying glaciers to find ways to
a. remove them as hazards to mountain homes.
b. change their pattern of movement.
c. keep them from thawing.
d. use them for fresh water.

_____ **10.** Icebergs differ from glaciers because glaciers
a. are made of ice.
b. cause damage.
c. cut grooves in valleys.
d. move from one location to another in cold areas.

_____ **11.** Icebergs are similar to glaciers in that
a. they contain much fresh water.
b. they slide down mountains.
c. they are found in the sea.
d. their shape fits the surrounding land.

_____ **12.** At a point where glaciers meet the sea,
a. icebergs form.
b. glaciers gain in size.
c. icebergs become glaciers.
d. glaciers leave the sea and move down into valleys.

_____ **13.** Valley glaciers develop
a. on a desert.
b. in the ocean.
c. on a mountain.
d. near the equator.

_____ **14.** Soil pore space reduces surface runoff because it
a. seals the soil surface and prevents runoff from soaking into the soil.
b. causes the soil to hold less water.
c. acts as a barrier to water.
d. permits soil to take up water.

_____ **15.** Seasons, soil types, numbers of plants, and soil condition are four factors that affect
a. precipitation.
b. condensation.
c. surface runoff.
d. icebergs.

_____ **16.** A type of rock considered to be permeable is
a. clay.
b. sandstone.
c. shale.
d. granite.

_____ **17.** An aquifer is a source of
a. groundwater.
b. soft water.
c. glaciers.
d. icebergs.

_____ **18.** Water is a solvent because it
a. contains carbon.
b. has plasticity.
c. is permeable.
d. has polarity.

_____ **19.** Groundwater will dissolve limestone if it combines with
a. hydrogen.
b. oxygen.
c. carbon dioxide.
d. sodium chloride.

_____ **20.** Hard water is different from soft water because it
a. comes from rainfall.
b. is present only in rivers.
c. contains minerals.
d. lacks dissolved minerals.

_____ **21.** A product not made with water is
a. soup.
b. coffee.
c. soft drinks.
d. plastic.

_____ **22**. A layer of which material would not make a good aquifer?
a. sandstone
b. shale
c. fractured limestone
d. gravel

_____ **23**. Holes drilled into aquifers where water gushes to the surface under its own pressure are called
a. springs.
b. ordinary wells.
c. geysers.
d. artesian wells.

_____ **24**. Water tables drop because of
a. heavy rains.
b. decreased air pressure.
c. droughts.
d. meltwater running into pore spaces.

_____ **25**. Stalagmites and stalactites are similar in that they
a. occur in lakes.
b. are formations.
c. are products of glaciation.
d. are simple solvents.

_____ **26**. A land area in which surface runoff drains into a river or system of rivers is called a(an)
a. aquifer.
b. stalagmite.
c. zone of saturation.
d. watershed.

_____ **27**. A crack in the surface of a glacier is called a(an)
a. crevice.
b. crevasse.
c. aquifer.
d. stalagmite.

_____ **28**. An open area between soil particles is called a
a. zone of aeration.
b. zone of salt water.
c. crevasse.
d. pore space.

_____ **29**. A shallow depression in the Earth's crust that has filled with water and that sunlight can penetrate to the bottom is called a(an)
a. lake.
b. reservoir.
c. pond.
d. artesian well.

_____ **30**. A deep depression in the Earth's crust that has filled with water and that sunlight cannot always penetrate to the bottom is called a(an)
a. lake.
b. reservoir.
c. pond.
d. artesian well.

TRUE OR FALSE

Determine whether each statement is true or false.

_____ **31**. Condensation is the process by which water changes into a gas.

_____ **32**. Icebergs are parts of a glacier.

_____ **33**. Cooling is largely responsible for ocean water being transformed into a vapor.

_____ **34**. When water evaporates from the ocean, salt is left behind.

_____ 35. Water vapor cannot be carried by wind.

_____ 36. As new snow piles up on top of old snow, some of the snow changes to ice.

_____ 37. Icebergs are large masses of frozen sea water.

_____ 38. Rivers, streams, and springs are types of standing water.

_____ 39. Watersheds prevent flooding.

_____ 40. Rapidly moving rivers can carry soil to remote locations.

COMPLETION

Fill in the word or number that best completes each statement.

______________ 41. The water present in the oceans of the Earth makes up _____ percent of all the water present.

______________ 42. Living things on the Earth cannot use ocean water because of the _____ present in it.

______________ 43. Moisture called _____ returns to the Earth in the form of rain, snow, or sleet.

______________ 44. A large body of moving ice and snow moving down a mountain is a _____.

______________ 45. Streams, springs, and _____ are examples of running water.

______________ 46. The hydrologic cycle constantly renews the Earth's supply of fresh _____.

______________ 47. As glaciers move down mountain valleys, they break open and form large _____, which are cracks in the ice.

______________ 48. As a valley glacier moves, _____ forms a stream from the melting of the glacier ice.

______________ 49. A thick sheet of ice called a(an) _____ glacier covers millions of square kilometers of area.

______________ 50. Huge ice chunks that break off from glaciers form _____ and drift out to sea.

______________ 51. Soil that has more _____ space will hold more water.

______________ 52. A(An) _____ is an area of land that drains runoff from rains into a stream or river.

______________ 53. A major problem with all of the fresh water on the Earth today is the danger of _____.

______________ 54. The term _____ is applied to water stored underground and provides a continual supply of fresh water.

____________ **55.** The _____ is the level to which groundwater has risen and saturated permeable soils.

____________ **56.** Large _____ form when groundwater enters cracks in limestone and dissolve it away, leaving large, underground rooms and underground passageways.

____________ **57.** A(An) _____ is a substance into which another substance will dissolve.

____________ **58.** Formations known as _____ hang from the top of caves and are formed from dissolved substances in groundwater.

____________ **59.** Water is classified as _____ if it contains large amounts of minerals and requires much soap to get a lot of suds.

____________ **60.** A(An) _____ is the resulting product of a substance being dissolved in a solvent.

USING SCIENCE SKILLS

Use the skills you have learned in the chapter to answer each question.

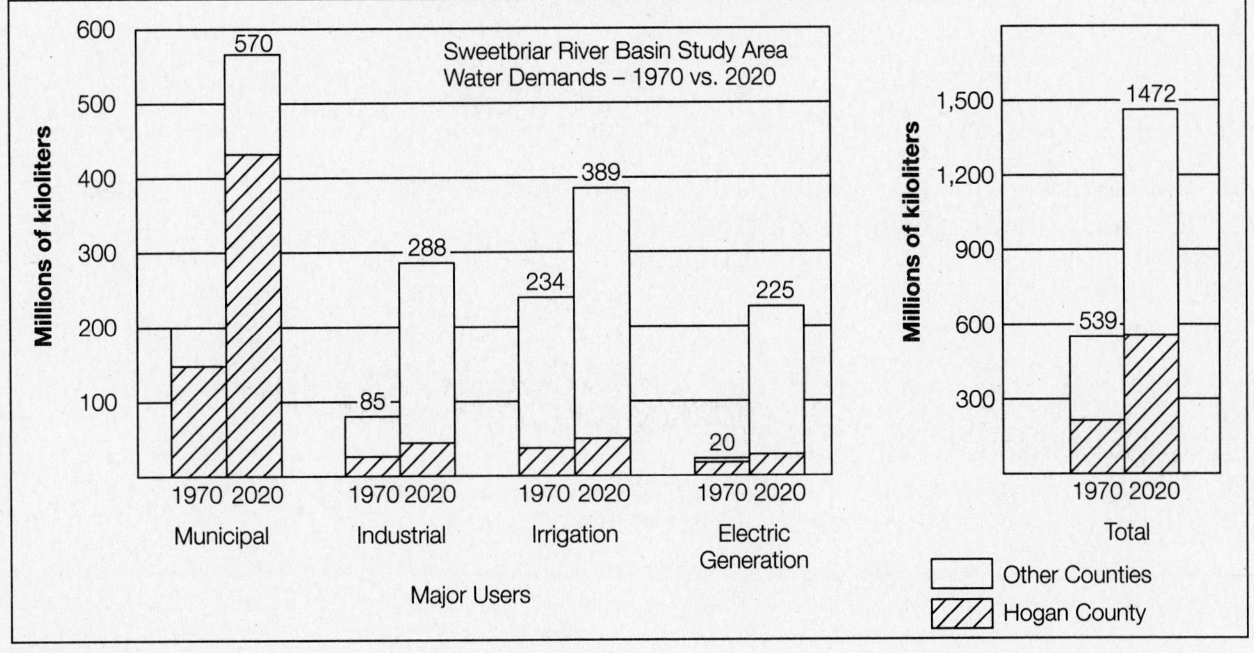

Figure 6

Running water is very much in demand. The Sweetbriar River serves Hogan County and eight surrounding counties in a river basin area with a continual supply of running water. Area planners conducted a study on the use of the river's water resources and projected what demands would be in 50 years. Figure 6 shows the results of the study.

61. In Figure 6, what is the combined Hogan County and surrounding area total demand for running water in 1970? In 2020?

62. Does Figure 6 show that Hogan County will surpass the other river basin counties in the total demand for water in 2020?

63. Does Figure 6 show that the other counties in the river basin had a higher water demand than Hogan County in 1970?

64. In Figure 6, which of the four major users of water demanded the most water in 1970? In 2020?

65. Does Figure 6 show that industry will lead the entire river basin area in the smallest increase in water demand in 2020? Why?

66. Based on the information in Figure 6, make a generalization about the growth of Hogan County compared to the rest of the river basin areas for the year 2020.

Name ______________________ Class ______________ Date ______________

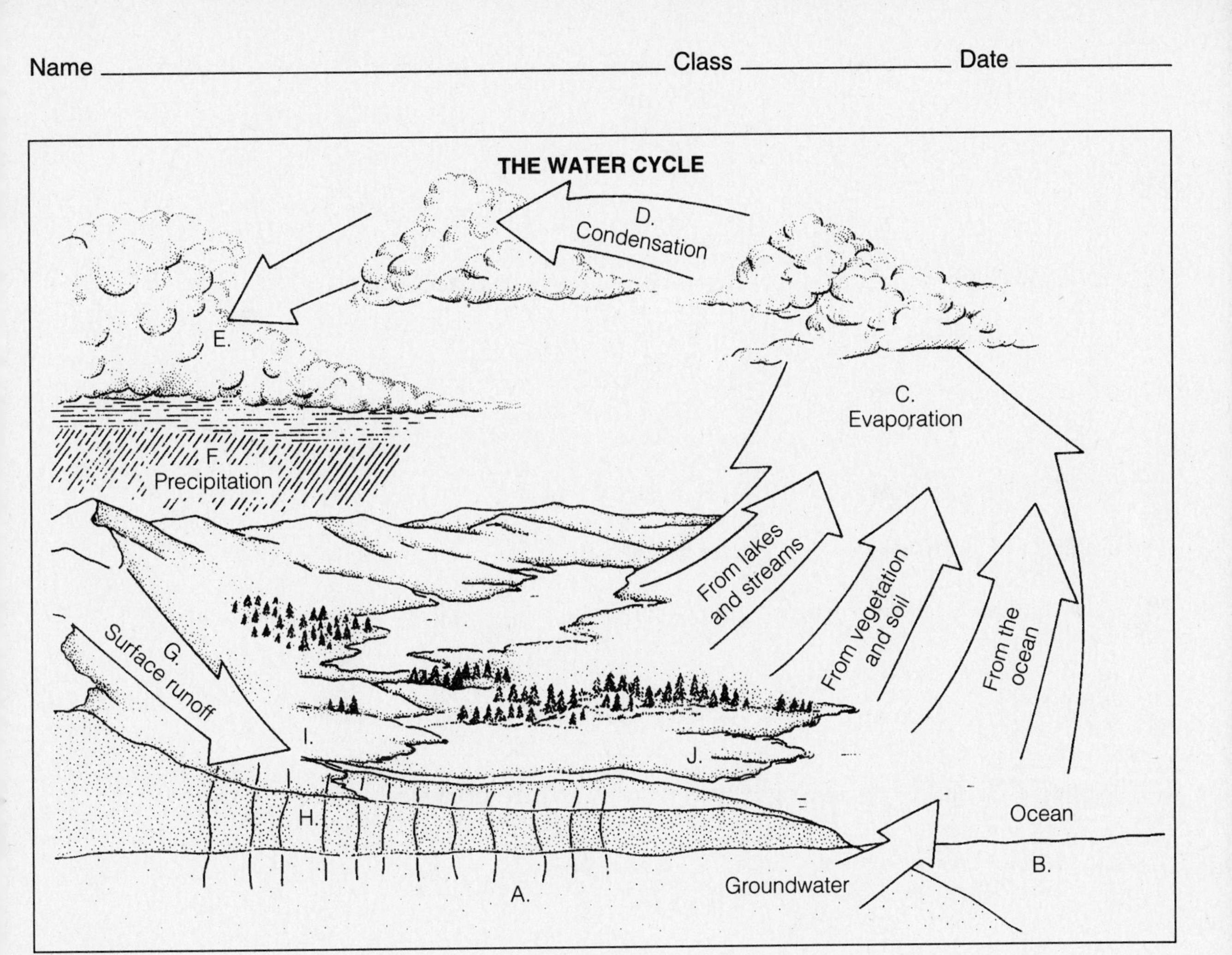

Figure 7

67. Identify the point in Figure 7 where water changes from a liquid to a gas.

68. Using the information given in Figure 7, explain how the area marked "A" gets replenished with fresh water.

69. At what point in Figure 7 does water return to the Earth as a liquid?

70. If there were a town located along the stream shown in Figure 7, would the quality of water be lower at point I or point J? Why?

71. How does Figure 7 show that physical changes take place in nature?

CRITICAL THINKING AND APPLICATION

Discuss each of the following in a brief paragraph.

72. How is a lake different from a reservoir?

73. Explain how polluted water gets recycled by nature into fresh water.

74. A major oil company is planning to build a crude oil transmission pipeline across the surface of the aquifer that supplies fresh water to your school or home. This pipeline will be a permanent installation. Should you be concerned about this development? Why or why not?

75. How are ponds and lakes alike? Different?

76. Why are reservoirs built near cities?

77. Explain at least three ways you can conserve water.

Name ____________________ Class ____________ Date ____________

78. You are the mayor of Batesville, a small city that gets all of its fresh water from the Fox River, which runs past the outskirts of town. Your city is growing rapidly every year. The river will no longer keep up with the demand for water in the next 5 years. There is no other river or lake nearby. As mayor, propose two possible solutions to this developing problem.

79. You are a driller for a water well company in central Oklahoma. It has become necessary for you to drill a water well on 60 acres of land belonging to a farmer so that 20 calves on the farm will have water to drink. As you get ready to drill, the following must be considered: permeable layer, impermeable layer, zone of aeration, pore space, zone of saturation, and water table. Using these terms, write a paragraph that discusses important considerations you must make while drilling so that you can be assured of a good and plentiful water supply.

80. Why does water have polarity and how does it help you in your daily life?

81. How is surface runoff water from land affected by the seasons, the condition of the soil, and the type of soil?

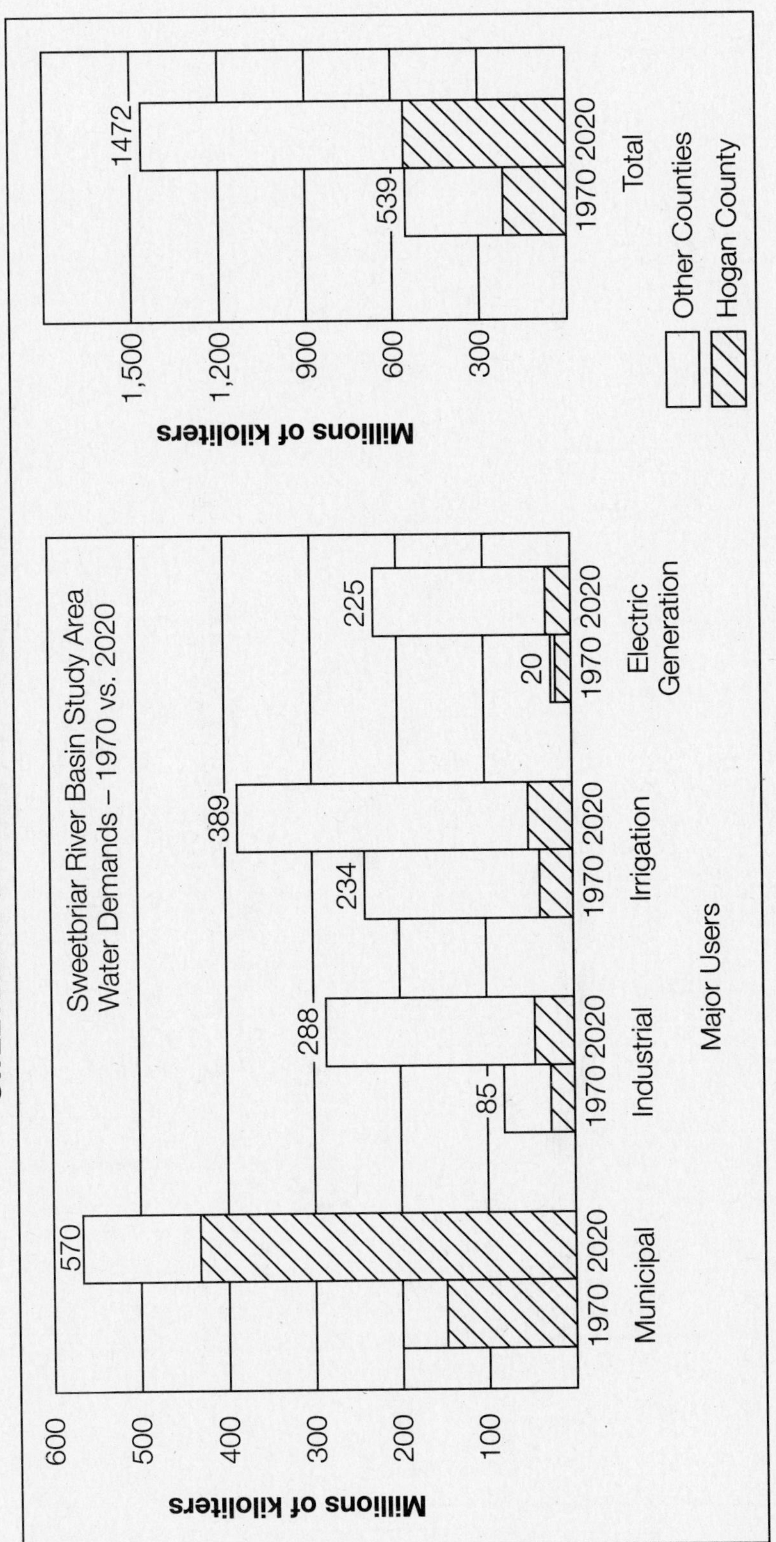

SWEETBRIAR RIVER BASIN WATER DEMANDS
Sweetbriar River Basin Study Area
Water Demands – 1970 vs. 2020
Millions of kiloliters
600
500
400
300
200
100
570
85
288
234
389
20
225
1970 2020
Municipal
Industrial
Irrigation
Electric
Generation
Major Users
1,500
1,200
900
600
300
539
1472
Total
Other Counties
Hogan County

Figure 6

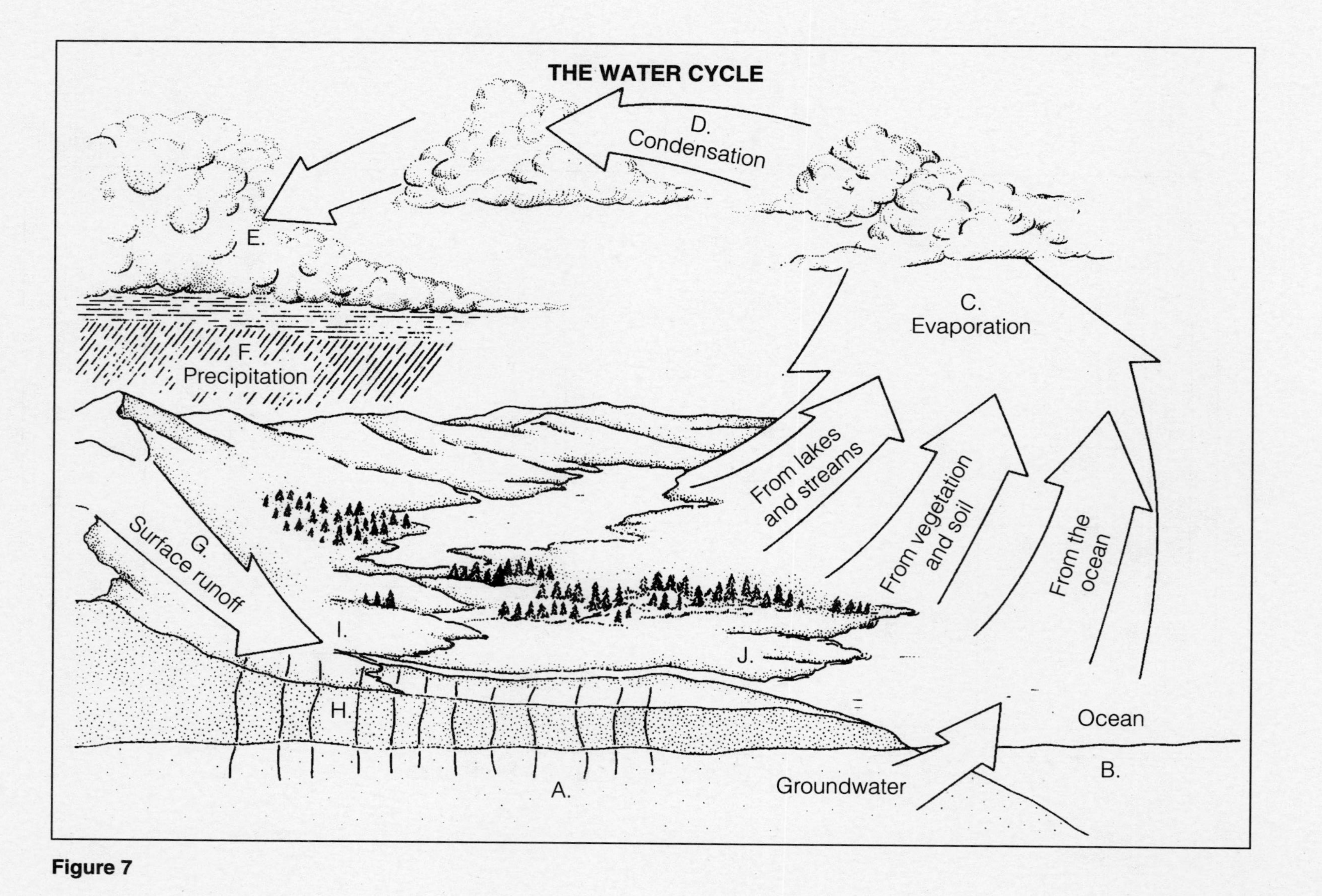

THE WATER CYCLE
D.
Condensation
E.
F.
Precipitation
C.
Evaporation
From lakes
and streams
From vegetation
and soil
From the
ocean
G.
Surface runoff
I.
J.
H.
Ocean
B.
Groundwater
A.

Figure 7

Answer Key

1. d
2. c
3. d
4. b
5. c
6. b
7. c
8. b
9. d
10. c
11. a
12. a
13. c
14. d
15. c
16. b
17. a
18. d
19. c
20. c
21. d
22. b
23. d
24. c
25. b
26. d
27. b
28. d
29. c
30. a
31. F
32. T
33. F
34. T
35. F
36. T
37. F
38. F
39. T
40. T
41. 97
42. salt
43. precipitation
44. glacier
45. rivers
46. water
47. crevasses
48. meltwater
49. continental
50. icebergs
51. pore
52. watershed
53. pollution
54. groundwater
55. water table
56. caverns
57. solvent
58. stalactites
59. hard
60. solution
61. 539 million kiloliters; 1472 million kiloliters
62. No.
63. Yes.
64. Hogan County Municipal/Hogan County Municipal
65. No, because the municipal users in counties other than Hogan will demand less water than industry in 2020.
66. Hogan County: greatest change will be in municipal users; least amount of change will be in electric generation users. Other counties: greatest change will be in irrigation users; least amount of change will be in municipal users.
67. C (evaporation)
68. As precipitation falls to the Earth, the Earth soaks up the water, allowing it to move down through the soil. Once it seeps through the soil, it becomes a part of the available groundwater in the Earth.

69. F (precipitation)
70. The water quality would probably be lower at point J because waste waters generated by the town would enter the stream at the town site and travel down river to the mouth. Thus, water at J is more likely to have pollutants than water at point I.
71. Figure 6 shows that water changes state twice—from a liquid to a gas in evaporation, and from a gas to a liquid in condensation.
72. Reservoirs differ from lakes in that they are artificially constructed storage areas of fresh water and are often built to assist in controlling heavy runoff during rainy periods. Lakes occur naturally or as a natural result of an activity such as building a dam.
73. Polluted water contains both the water and the pollutants dissolved in it. As this water gets heated by the sun, the water on the surface changes to a vapor and rises into the atmosphere, ultimately to return to the Earth as rain. The pollutants dissolved in the water do not turn into vapor as the water does, thus staying behind. In this way, polluted water becomes recycled as fresh water.
74. Student responses may vary. Student responses should mention concern about the pipeline. Even though the pipeline will be intact upon completion, there is a strong chance that it could rupture on its own, be hit by something, or in some other way be unintentionally opened, releasing the contents of the pipeline to the ground below. The spilled oil could easily enter the aquifer, permanently damaging the freshwater supply.
75. Lake are large, deep depressions in the Earth that are filled with fresh water; ponds are shallow depressions, smaller, not as deep, and have more plant growth present.
76. Some cities are plagued with flooding problems, and reservoirs can be built in the drainage zone to control the heavy runoff. Some cities have a shortage of drinking water, so a reservoir built nearby provides a source of fresh water as well as water that can be used for irrigation of agricultural crops in the area. Reservoirs may also store water to be used to generate electric power.
77. Student answers will vary. Some possible answers include: not washing cars frequently, washing clothes with a reduced water level in the washing machine, using less water to wash dishes, shortening the time spent in the shower, eliminating needless watering of lawns, installing a water-saving showerhead.
78. One solution might be to initiate the construction of a large freshwater reservoir as a cooperative effort between the city and the federal government. This would provide the much needed water. Another solution might be to explore the drilling of deep wells into the strata below the city to find large sources of acceptable fresh water. A third solution might be to explore the construction of a freshwater pipeline to transport water from distant natural lakes, rivers, or reservoirs to your city. Perhaps irrigation canals could be built to transport water from remote locations to the city.
79. Selecting a site for a water well includes making sure you are over layers of the Earth that are permeable with good pore spaces so that water may flow into your well quickly and abundantly. While drilling, it is desirable to penetrate a good zone of aeration in the layer containing fresh water. Once you find good water you want to stop drilling so that you do not go through an impermeable layer that keeps water available for your well. It is necessary that the water collect above the impermeable layer and form a good zone of saturation for you to draw water from with your pump. If you pump water too quickly, the water table will drop significantly, indicating that the water supply is limited.
80. Water has polarity because the oxygen end of the molecule is negatively charged, while the hydrogen end is positively charged. These polarized ends help you because they help make water and another substance combine to form a solution. This is important because certain foods, medicines, soaps, and other necessary substances must be combined with water in order to be used.
81. During the times of the year when land areas experience much rain and meltwater, runoff is great. When the soil is extremely dry, runoff will be minimal, but when it is wet, runoff will be very high. Permeable soils like sand soak up large quantities of water, reducing the amount of water runoff. Clay soils do not absorb a lot of water, so runoff from these areas is very high.

Contents

Name ____________________ Class ____________ Date ____________

Chapter Test

CHAPTER 4 ■ Earth's Landmasses

MULTIPLE CHOICE

Write the letter of the correct answer on the line at the left.

_____ **1.** The measure of distance east or west of the prime meridian is called
a. latitude. c. contour interval.
b. longitude. d. parallel.

_____ **2.** The 180th meridian is called the
a. prime meridian. c. North Pole.
b. equator. d. international date line.

_____ **3.** If it is 3 PM in a certain time zone, what time is it two time zones to the west?
a. 5 PM c. 2 PM
b. 4 PM d. 1 PM

_____ **4.** A flat land area not far above sea level is called a
a. plateau. c. mountain belt.
b. plain. d. relief.

_____ **5.** A flat representation that shows the different shapes, sizes, and reliefs of a land surface is called a(an)
a. equal-area projection. c. topographic map.
b. Mercator projection. d. legend.

_____ **6.** Closely spaced contour lines indicate a
a. stream. c. gentle slope.
b. plain. d. steep slope.

_____ **7.** The latitude labeled 0° is the
a. prime meridian. c. North Pole.
b. equator. d. international date line.

_____ **8.** Which of the following is a continent, a landmass, and a country?
a. South America c. Australia
b. Greenland d. Antarctica

_____ **9.** The Appalachians are examples of a(an)
a. mountain system. c. mountain belt.
b. mountain range. d. interior plain.

_____ **10.** Which of the following correctly shows coastline shapes but distorts areas far from the equator?
a. equal-area projection c. Mercator projection
b. globe d. topographic map

COMPLETION

Complete each statement on the line at the left.

_______________ **1.** The difference in elevation from one contour line to the next is called the _____.

_______________ **2.** Short lines drawn perpendicular to contour lines that indicate a depression are called _____.

_______________ **3.** A map that correctly represents area but not shape is called a(an) _____.

_______________ **4.** A broad, flat area of land that rises more than 600 m above sea level is called a(an) _____.

_______________ **5.** A map is an example of a(an) _____, or representation of a three-dimensional object on a flat surface.

TRUE OR FALSE

Determine whether each statement is true or false. If it is true, write T. If it is false, change the underlined word or words to make the statement true.

_____ _______________ **1.** The meanings of symbols on a map are given in the legend.

_____ _______________ **2.** A group of mountain ranges in one area is called a mountain system.

_____ _______________ **3.** The difference in a region's elevations is called its longitude.

_____ _______________ **4.** North America and Asia are examples of continents.

_____ _______________ **5.** A large area of very old rock exposed at the surface of a continent is called a shield.

Name ______________________________ Class ______________ Date __________

USING SCIENCE SKILLS: Interpreting Maps, Relating Concepts

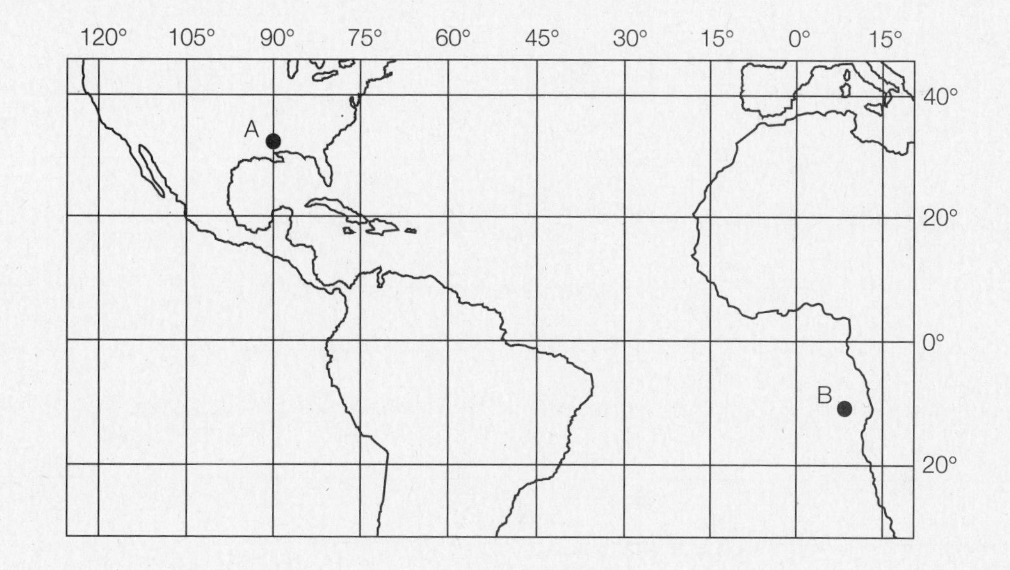

1. What are the straight lines running from left to right called? ______________

2. What are the straight lines running up and down called? ______________

3. What are the latitude and longitude of point A? ______________

   Point B? ______________

4. Mark the following locations on the map. C: 10° north latitude and 15° east longitude; D: 20° south latitude and 110° west longitude.

ESSAY

Write a brief paragraph discussing each of the following statements or questions.

1. Contrast mountains, plateaus, and plains.

____

____

____

____

____

____

____

2. What are the differences between a Mercator projection, an equal-area projection, and a topographic map?

3. What is the difference between a continent and a landmass? Give two examples of each.

4. Under what circumstances would a globe be more useful than a map?

5. Why is a larger contour interval used for mapping mountains than is used for mapping flat areas?

1. b **2.** d **3.** d **4.** b **5.** c **6.** d **7.** b **8.** c **9.** a **10.** c

COMPLETION

1. contour interval **2.** hachures **3.** equal-area projection **4.** plateau **5.** projection

TRUE OR FALSE

1. T **2.** T **3.** F, relief **4.** T **5.** T

USING SCIENCE SKILLS

1. parallels **2.** meridians **3.** A: 30° north latitude, 90° west longitude; B: 10° south latitude, 10° east longitude **4.** Check student maps.

ESSAY

1. Mountains are high-relief landscape regions that must rise at least 600 m above the surrounding area and must have narrow summits and steep slopes. Plateaus are broad, flat, low-relief landscapes that are more than 600 m above sea level. Plains are flat, low-relief landscapes not far above sea level. **2.** A Mercator projection correctly shows the shapes of coastlines but distorts the size of areas far from the equator. An equal-area projection shows area correctly but distorts shape. A topographic map show shape and size, as well as other features, and shows the relief of the land. **3.** A continent is a large land area that measure millions of square kilometers and that rises a considerable distance above sea level. Landmasses are separate bodies of land surrounded by water and may be made up of an island, a continent, or several continents joined together. The continents are Europe, Asia, Africa, North America, South America, Australia, and Antarctica. Example of landmasses are Australia, Europe, Asia, and Africa together; and North and South America together. **4.** A globe is more useful when a completely accurate representation of the Earth's landmasses and bodies of water in correct shape and proportion are needed. **5.** The rate of increase in elevation is much greater when depicting mountains rather than flat areas. As such, if the contour intervals are small, there will be too many contour lines on the map to make it clearly understandable.
Write the letter of the answer that best completes each statement.

Name ______________________ Class __________ Date __________

Test Bank Test

CHAPTER 4 ■ Earth's Landmasses

MULTIPLE CHOICE

Write the letter of the answer that best completes each statement.

_____ **1.** The difference between a continent and an island is
- a. the height of the land above the sea.
- b. that islands are surrounded by water.
- c. the size of the landmass.
- d. that islands have volcanoes present.

_____ **2.** An example of the way technology has changed a part of the surface of the Earth is
- a. mountains.
- b. plains.
- c. plateaus.
- d. dams.

_____ **3.** The North American and South American continents are joined at a point where
- a. Central America and South America meet.
- b. the United States and Central America meet.
- c. South America and the United States meet.
- d. the equator crosses South America.

_____ **4.** The Earth contains how many major landmasses?
- a. two
- b. three
- c. four
- d. five

_____ **5.** In terms of size, the largest landmass on Earth is a(an)
- a. plateau.
- b. mountain.
- c. island.
- d. continent.

_____ **6.** The continent of Eurasia includes
- a. Europe and Africa.
- b. Europe and Australia.
- c. Asia and Europe.
- d. Asia and Africa.

_____ **7.** The smallest continent on Earth is
- a. South America.
- b. Antarctica.
- c. Australia.
- d. North America.

_____ **8.** Each continent on Earth has a shield that
- a. contains only coastal plains.
- b. forms the core of the continent.
- c. is marked by extremely high elevation.
- d. forms the outer border of the continent.

_____ **9.** Lines of longitude found on a map are the distance
- a. north and south of the equator.
- b. east and west of the prime meridian.
- c. north and south of the International Date Line.
- d. east and west of the equator.

_____ **10.** Finding a place on the Earth requires that you know
a. the longitude and the location of the prime meridian.
b. the longitude and the location of the International Date Line.
c. the latitude and the location of the equator.
d. the longitude and the latitude.

_____ **11.** An imaginary line drawn east to west halfway between the North Pole and South Pole is the
a. longitude.
b. prime meridian.
c. International Date Line.
d. equator.

_____ **12.** Latitude is measured
a. north and south of the equator.
b. beginning at the 180° west of the prime meridian.
c. east and west of the prime meridian.
d. from the International Date Line.

_____ **13.** The scale on any map shows
a. how to use map symbols.
b. distances between places.
c. directions respective to north on the map.
d. the type of map projection.

_____ **14.** The legend on any map helps you to
a. find the elevations of places.
b. locate north and south.
c. interpret symbols and their meaning.
d. determine distances between places.

_____ **15.** Steep slopes on a topographic map occur where contour lines are
a. colored black.
b. far apart.
c. divided.
d. close together.

_____ **16.** Topographic maps are unique in that they show
a. highways and roads.
b. large and small buildings.
c. rivers and streams.
d. changes in elevation.

_____ **17.** All points on a contour line have
a. the same elevation.
b. a small depression.
c. different elevations.
d. an elevation above 400 m.

_____ **18.** A depression appears on a topographic map as
a. a series of straight lines.
b. curved lines in a circle.
c. hachures pointing to the inside of a loop.
d. closely spaced and looped contours.

_____ **19.** To represent a hill on a topographic map, you would draw
a. straight lines spaced far apart.
b. concentric loops with hachures.
c. lines that represent closed loops.
d. a series of lines very close together.

_____ **20.** If you draw a map and you want to signify that the black square you drew on the map is a house, you must include the square in the
a. contour line.
b. scale.
c. legend.
d. hachure.

_____ **21.** When drawing roads and buildings on a topographic map, you should draw them in
a. red.
b. blue.
c. green.
d. black.

_____ **22.** To travel from the North Pole to the equator, you would have to travel from
a. 90° N to 60° N.
b. 0° to 90° N.
c. 90° N to 0°.
d. 60° N to 0°.

_____ **23.** If Greenland is at latitude 75° N, and a part of South America is at latitude 30° S, there is a difference in latitude of
a. 105°.
b. 45°.
c. 30°.
d. 125°.

_____ **24.** Los Angeles, California, is two time zones west of Dallas, Texas. If it is 8:00 AM in Los Angeles, what time is it in Dallas?
a. 6:00 AM
b. 10:00 AM
c. 11:00 AM
d. 5:00 AM

_____ **25.** If city "A" is at longitude 75° W, and city "B" is at longitude 120° W, how many hours are they apart in time?
a. 1 hour
b. 2 hours
c. 3 hours
d. 5 hours

_____ **26.** Lines appearing on a Mercator projection map that run from east to west are
a. contour.
b. meridians.
c. legends.
d. parallels.

_____ **27.** Parallels on a map or globe cannot exceed
a. 0°.
b. 45°.
c. 60°.
d. 90°.

_____ **28.** Swamps and woods appear on a topographic map in
a. red.
b. green.
c. black.
d. blue.

_____ **29.** The number of continents on the Earth is
a. two.
b. four.
c. seven.
d. ten.

_____ **30.** The shape of the Earth's surface is called its
a. topography.
b. relief.
c. contour line.
d. projection.

TRUE OR FALSE

Determine whether each statement is true or false.

_____ **31.** Europe, Australia, and Asia compose the largest landmass on the surface of the Earth.

_____ **32.** The Antarctic icecap is the largest icecap in the world.

_____ **33.** Continents, mountains, and plains are the three main types of landscape regions.

_____ **34.** The elevation of the coastal plains is lower than the elevation of the interior plains.

_____ **35.** The longitude of the prime meridian is found on the globe of the Earth at 180°.

_____ **36.** Lines of latitude that run east to west on the world map are parallel to each other.

_____ **37.** Correct shapes of landmasses are shown on an equal-area projection map.

_____ **38.** On topographic maps, elevation numbers decrease toward the center of a depression.

_____ **39.** As you travel west, your subtract one hour for each 15° of latitude.

_____ **40.** The difference in latitude between the North and the South poles is 180°.

COMPLETION

Fill in the word or number that best completes each statement.

______________ **41.** The continents on the Earth are joined together on the surface to form large areas called _____.

______________ **42.** The most recently discovered continent is _____.

______________ **43.** Combined together, Europe, Africa, and _____ make up the largest landmass on the Earth.

______________ **44.** A(An) _____ is a mass of rock rising more than 600 m above the surrounding land.

______________ **45.** The continent of Australia is completely surrounded by _____.

______________ **46.** Topography is the features and shape of the Earth's _____.

______________ **47.** The difference in a region's elevation is known as _____.

______________ **48.** Mountains are easy to identify as they have narrow _____ on top and steep _____.

______________ **49.** Mount Everest is the _____ mountain in the world.

______________ **50.** Along the coasts of continents near sea level, the low, flat areas of land are referred to as _____.

______________ **51.** Mount Vesuvius in Italy is an example of a(an) _____ mountain.

Name ______________________ Class ____________ Date ____________

_______________ **52.** A drawing that shows the Earth's surface on a flat sheet of paper is a _____.

_______________ **53.** The continent of North America is connected to the continent of _____.

_______________ **54.** A(An) _____ is a type of landscape region that features a large area of flat land at a high elevation.

_______________ **55.** A drawing that shows the different shapes and sizes of a land surface is known as a(an) _____ map.

_______________ **56.** The locations, shapes, and sizes of all the Earth's landmasses are shown on a(an) _____, which is a spherical model of the Earth.

_______________ **57.** The _____ of a map compares the distance on a map to the actual distance on the Earth's surface.

_______________ **58.** A line on a map of the world from pole to pole and passing through Greenwich, England, is always referred to as the _____ meridian.

_______________ **59.** Each of the 24 zones of 15° of longitude are identified as _____ zones.

_______________ **60.** If you wanted to represent a small depression on a topographic map, you would show it by putting in _____ on the map.

USING SCIENCE SKILLS

Use the skills you have developed in the chapter to answer each question or statement.

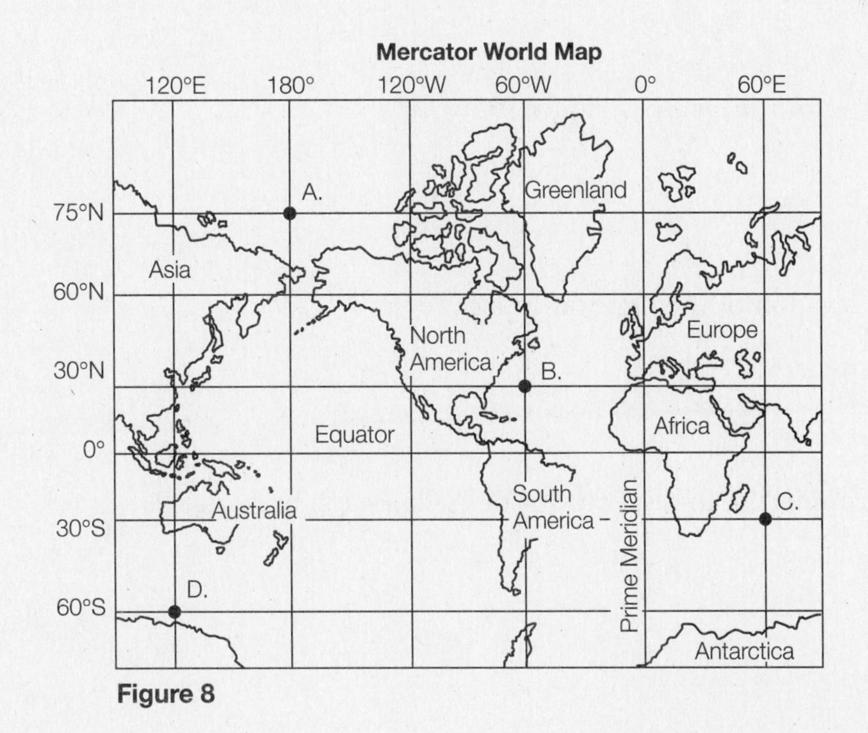

Figure 8

61. What two variables are displayed on the axes of the map shown in Figure 8?

62. A ship is anchored at point "C" on the map in Figure 8. Using your map-reading skills, state the exact position of the ship.

63. Compare the positions of Europe and central Africa on the map in Figure 8.

64. How much difference in latitude is there between points A and D in Figure 8?

65. Is location B in Figure 8 at 60° latitude? Explain.

66. Using Figure 9, describe the shape, location, and features of Egg Island.

67. What is the contour interval in Figure 9?

68. What is the elevation of the highway in Figure 9?

69. At what elevation is the lowest contour of Walla Beach in Figure 9?

Name ______________________ Class ______________ Date ______________

70. In Figure 9, how much change in elevation is there between the school at point A and the house at point B?

71. There is a severe storm brewing in the south and tides are expected to rise 3 m. How many buildings in Figure 9 will have water in them due to high tide?

72. What is the distance between the school and the marina in Figure 9?

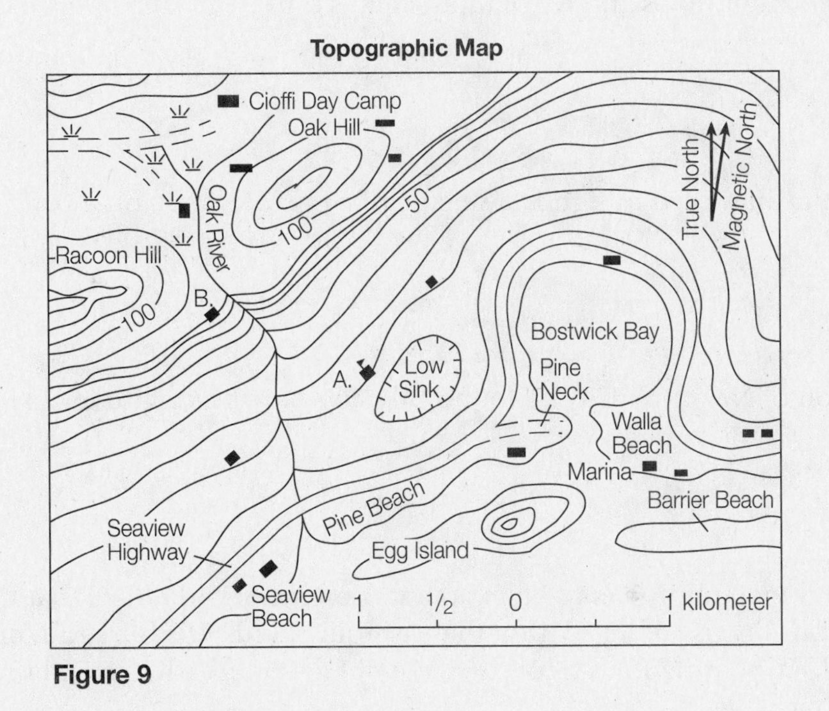

Figure 9

CRITICAL THINKING AND APPLICATION

Discuss each of the following in a brief paragraph.

73. Explain how maps aid us in learning about the Earth.

74. Why is it necessary for a topographic map to have a legend?

75. Dallas, Texas, is one time zone east of Denver, Colorado. If you depart Dallas by plane at 9:00 AM for a 3-hour flight to Denver, what time will it be in Denver when you land?

76. Denver, New York City, Los Angeles, and Dallas are four cities in the United States. Each city is in a different time zone, but the sun rises at the same time in each city. List the cities in the order in which they will see the morning sun, starting with the first. Why do the cities see the sun in this order?

77. Explain how Mercator maps and topographic maps differ.

78. How are contour lines used to signify a steep cliff or gentle slope on a contour map?

79. Can the location of New York City be found by using only its longitude? Explain.

80. While studying a topographic map of an area in Colorado, you notice that the highest full circle contour line is 750 m. Within that contour stands Missouri Hill, marked with an X at its peak. If your map has a contour interval of 250 m, what would the maximum height of Missouri Hill be?

81. Describe or draw the topographic map symbols for a house, a railroad, a school, and an unpaved road.

82. The following is a description of a small area. An oval pond is seen on a flat basin area. To the left of the pond is a steep cliff that rises from its base elevation at 20 m to an elevation of 600 m at its peak. The opposite side of the peak has a gentle slope. To the right of the pond is a round, dome-shaped hill that rises from an elevation of 300 m to 500 m. A railroad passes between the pond and the hill on the right and also between the pond and the hill on the left. Draw a topographic map to represent the scene described above. Use a contour interval of 200 m.

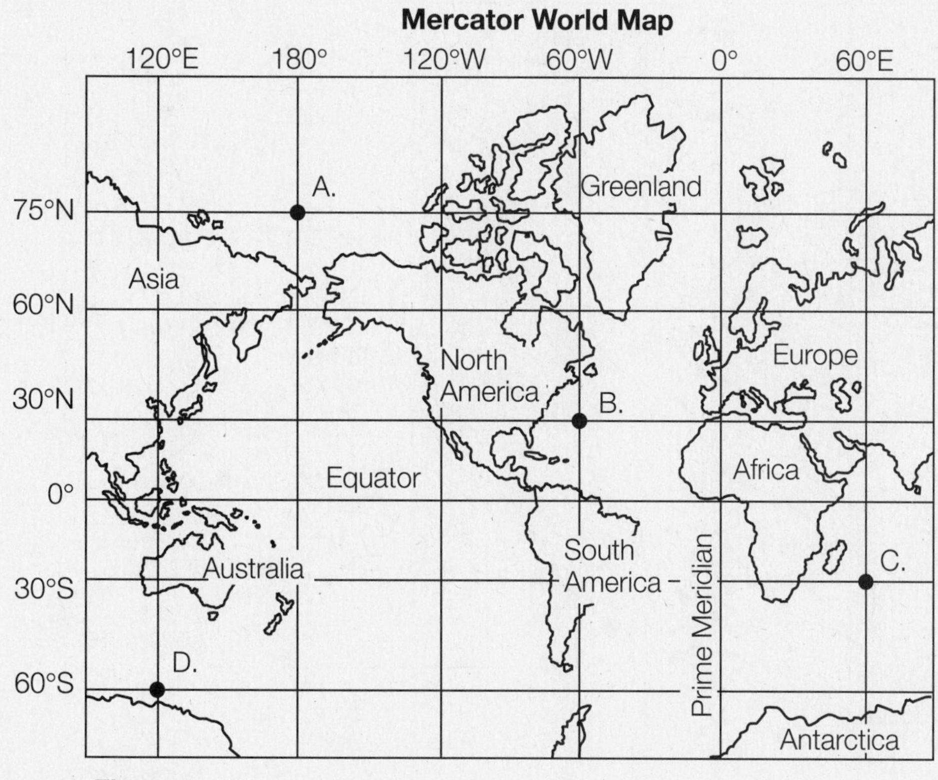
Mercator World Map
120°E
180°
120°W
60°W
0°
60°E
75°N
60°N
30°N
0°
30°S
60°S
A.
B.
C.
D.
Asia
Greenland
North America
Europe
Africa
Equator
Australia
South America
Prime Meridian
Antarctica

Figure 8

Topographic Map

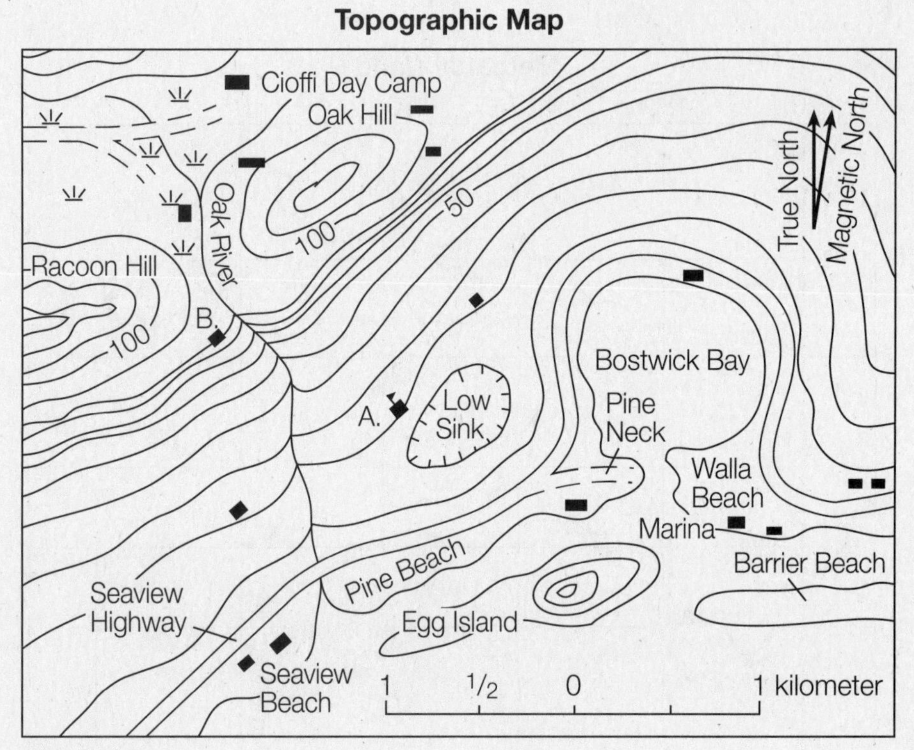

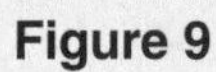

Figure 9

Answer Key

1. c
2. d
3. a
4. c
5. d
6. c
7. c
8. b
9. b
10. d
11. d
12. a
13. b
14. c
15. d
16. d
17. a
18. c
19. c
20. c
21. d
22. c
23. a
24. b
25. c
26. d
27. d
28. b
29. c
30. a
31. F
32. T
33. F
34. T
35. F
36. T
37. F
38. T
39. T
40. T

41. landmasses
42. Antarctica
43. Asia
44. mountain
45. water
46. surface
47. relief
48. summits, slope
49. highest
50. coastal plains
51. volcanic
52. map
53. South America
54. plateau
55. topographical
56. globe
57. scale
58. prime
59. time
60. hachures
61. latitude and longitude
62. 60° E, 30° S
63. Most of both Africa and Europe are between 0° and 60° E longitude, but their latitudes are different. Africa lies between 0° and 30° N latitude, while Europe lies between 30° N and 60° N latitude.
64. 135°
65. Point B is not at 60° latitude. It is at 30° latitude. It is at 60° longitude.
66. Egg Island is oblong in shape and runs northeast to southwest. The island has two buildings on the north shore and a hill or mound at the northeast end of the island. The hill is at least 30 m in elevation above the level of the water.
67. 10 m
68. Between 0 and 10 m
69. 0 m (sea level)
70. 60 m

71. 10
72. 1½ to 2 km
73. Maps are scale models of the Earth. They provide us with details about small as well as large areas of the Earth.
74. The legend helps one recognize different natural and constructed structures that are present in the area covered by the map.
75. 11:00 AM
76. New York City, Dallas, Denver, Los Angeles. The sun rises in this order because the Earth is rotating on its axis from west to east, and New York City is farthest east of the four cities listed.
77. Mercator maps show land and water areas but not in their correct shape, while topographic maps show the relief of the land and the various features present.
78. The elevation of a steep cliff changes very rapidly with distance, so contour lines must be very close together. The elevation of gentle slopes changes very little with distance, so contour lines are drawn with wide spaces between them.
79. No, because longitude will only tell you how far east or west of the prime meridian New York is. It fails to tell you how far north or south of the equator New York is located.
80. 1000 m
81. a. a solid square; b. horizontal line with vertical slashes; c. solid square with small flag on top; d. two parallel, dashed lines
82. Students' maps will vary.

Contents

CHAPTER 5 ■ Earth's Interior

Name ______________________ Class ______________ Date ____________

Chapter Test

CHAPTER 5 ■ Earth's Interior

MULTIPLE CHOICE

Write the letter of the correct answer on the line at the left.

_____ **1.** Iron and nickel make up the
- a. mantle.
- b. lithosphere.
- c. core.
- d. crust.

_____ **2.** The temperature of the inner core is roughly
- a. –200°C.
- b. 0°C.
- c. 1000°C.
- d. 5000°C.

_____ **3.** The inner core is probably responsible for the Earth's
- a. magnetic field.
- b. low density.
- c. tides.
- d. weather.

_____ **4.** The lithosphere is made up of
- a. liquid.
- b. gases.
- c. unbroken solid.
- d. solid plates.

_____ **5.** The average thickness of the crust is
- a. less than 32 km.
- c. 500 km.
- c. 3200 km.
- d. 5000 km.

_____ **6.** The density of the mantle
- a. increases with depth.
- b. decreases with depth.
- c. is constant.
- d. cannot be estimated.

_____ **7.** Life on the Earth exists on or within the
- a. mantle and crust.
- b. mantle, crust, and outer core.
- c. mantle only.
- d. crust only.

_____ **8.** Two of the most abundant elements in the crust are
- a. nickel and iron.
- b. silicon and oxygen.
- c. carbon and oxygen.
- d. silicon and nickel.

_____ **9.** The second-deepest layer of the Earth is the
- a. crust.
- b. Moho.
- c. mantle.
- d. inner core.

_____ **10.** Scientists determined the structure of the core by studying
- a. gravitational effects.
- b. seismic waves.
- c. the Earth's magnetic field.
- d. temperature effects.

COMPLETION

Complete each statement on the line at the left.

_____________ 1. Earthquake waves are recorded by an instrument called a(an) _____.

_____________ 2. The innermost layer of the Earth is the _____.

_____________ 3. The thinnest layer of the Earth is the _____.

_____________ 4. The topmost part of the Earth, which is broken up into plates, is the _____.

_____________ 5. As the depth of the mantle increases, temperature and pressure _____.

TRUE OR FALSE

Determine whether each statement is true or false. If it is true, write T. If it is false, change the underlined word or words to make the statement true.

_____ _____________ 1. S waves are stopped by liquids.

_____ _____________ 2. The Moho is the boundary between the Earth's outermost layer and the outer core.

_____ _____________ 3. The outer core is liquid.

_____ _____________ 4. Rock in the mantle has an ability to flow, which called plasticity.

_____ _____________ 5. The mantle is denser than the crust.

Name ______________________ Class __________ Date __________

USING SCIENCE SKILLS: Making Measurements, Interpreting Diagrams, Interpreting Graphs

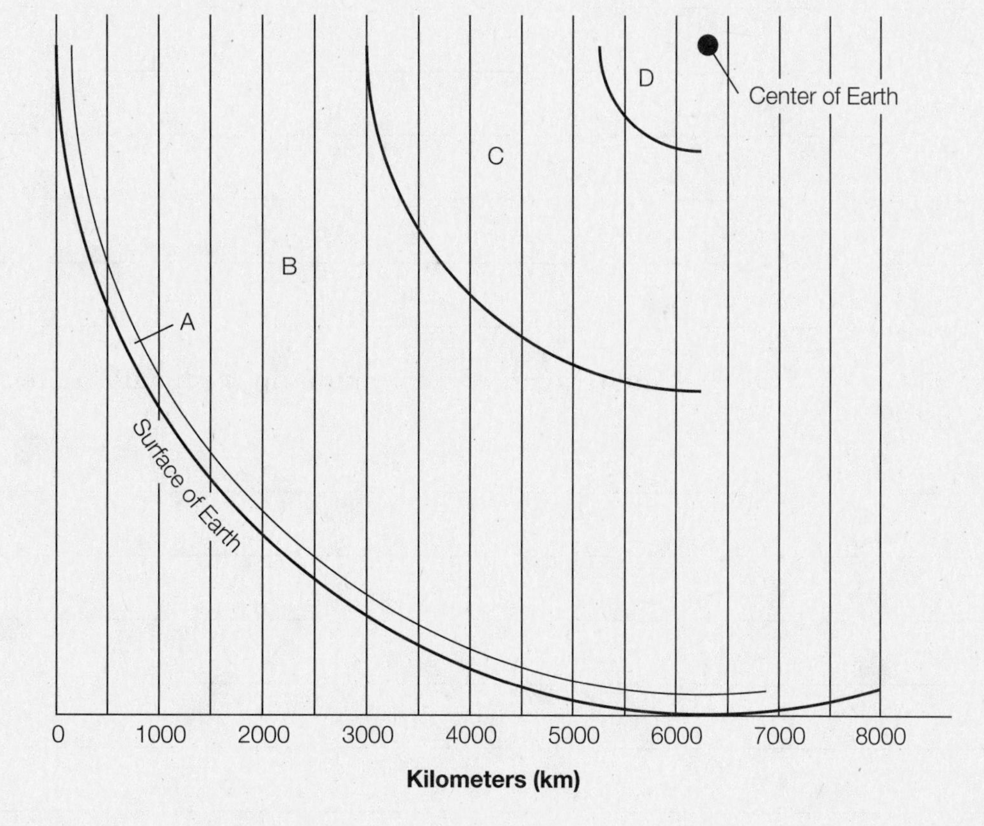

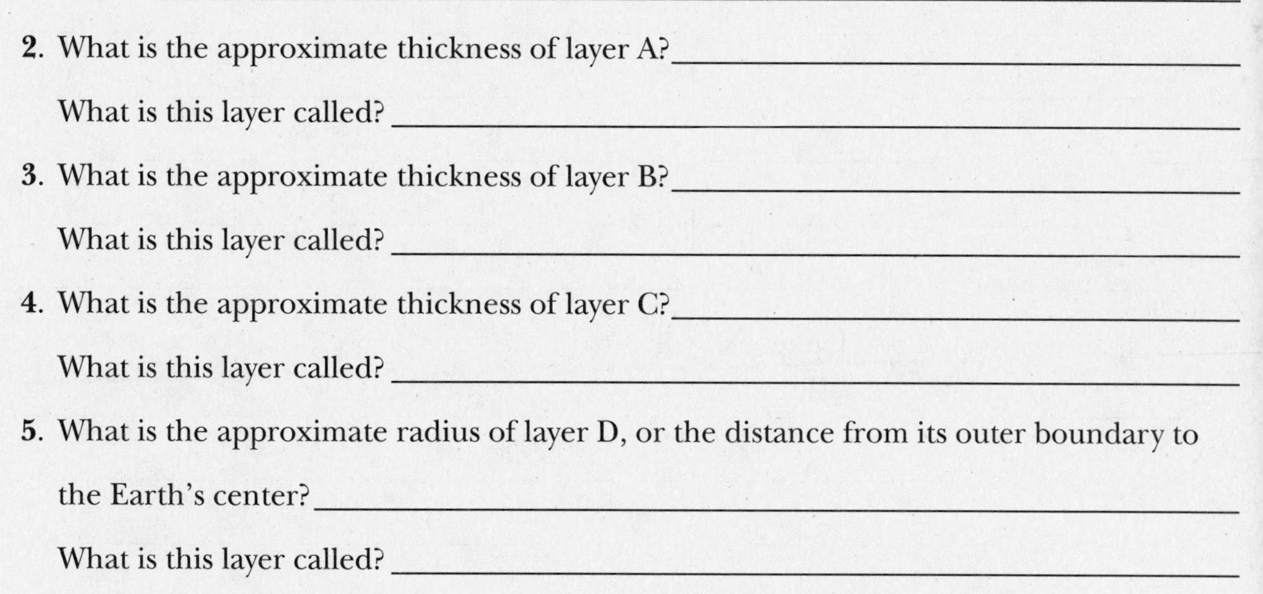

1. What is the approximate radius of the Earth, or the distance from its surface to its center? ______________________

2. What is the approximate thickness of layer A? ______________________

What is this layer called? ______________________

3. What is the approximate thickness of layer B? ______________________

What is this layer called? ______________________

4. What is the approximate thickness of layer C? ______________________

What is this layer called? ______________________

5. What is the approximate radius of layer D, or the distance from its outer boundary to the Earth's center? ______________________

What is this layer called? ______________________

ESSAY

Write a brief paragraph discussing each of the following statements.

1. Explain how P waves and S waves revealed information about the Earth's structure.

2. Contrast the composition of and temperature conditions in the mantle, outer core, and inner core.

3. Compare continental crust and oceanic crust.

4. Compare the formation of igneous, sedimentary, and metamorphic rocks.

Answer Key

MULTIPLE CHOICE

1. c **2.** d **3.** a **4.** d **5.** a **6.** a **7.** d **8.** b **9.** c **10.** b

COMPLETION

1. seismograph **2.** inner core **3.** crust **4.** lithosphere **5.** increase

TRUE OR FALSE

1. T **2.** F, mantle **3.** T **4.** T **5.** T

USING SCIENCE SKILLS

1. 6400 km **2.** generally less than 50 km; the crust **3.** 2900 km; the mantle **4.** 2250 km; the outer core **5.** 1300 km; the inner core

ESSAY

1. P waves and S waves both move readily through solids. P waves are slowed by liquids and S waves are stopped by them. At a certain depth (2900 km), P waves are slowed down and S waves are stopped. This indicates a liquid layer, the core, beginning at that depth. At a greater depth (over 5000 km), P waves more more quickly, indicating a solid layer, the inner core, beginning at that depth. **2.** The mantle is mostly silicon, oxygen, iron, and magnesium, and ranges in temperature from about 870°C to about 2200°C. The outer core is liquid iron and nickel and ranges in temperature from 2200°C to 5000°C. The inner core is solid iron and nickel and is about 5000°C. **3.** Continental crust, or crust beneath the continents, is about 32 km thick, on the average. It is made up mostly of silicon, oxygen, aluminum, calcium, sodium, and potassium. Oceanic crust, or crust beneath the continents, is only about 8 km thick, on the average. It is made up mostly of silicon, oxygen, iron, and magnesium. **4.** Igneous rocks form when hot liquid rock from deep within the Earth cools and hardens as it reaches the surface. Sedimentary rocks form when sediments are pressed and cemented together by the weight of other rock layers. Metamorphic rocks form when igneous and sedimentary rocks are changed by heat, pressure, or the action of chemicals.

Name ______________________ Class ____________ Date ____________

Test Bank Test

CHAPTER 5 ■ Earth's Interior

MULTIPLE CHOICE

Write the letter of the answer that best completes each statement.

_____ **1.** The core of the Earth can be studied by
a. drilling into it.
b. examining core samples.
c. chemically analyzing Earth core rocks.
d. studying core seismic wave patterns.

_____ **2.** As shock waves travel through the Earth they
a. all travel at the same speed.
b. all arrive at recording devices at the same time.
c. penetrate the depths of the Earth and then return to the surface.
d. penetrate the depths of the Earth and disappear in the inner core.

_____ **3.** Which of the following is not a distinct layer of the Earth?
a. outer core
b. mantle
c. Moho
d. crust

_____ **4.** The core of the Earth is composed of
a. magnesium and silicon.
b. iron and silicon.
c. nickel and oxygen.
d. nickel and iron.

_____ **5.** Two layers of the Earth that are made up of the same two major elements are the
a. mantle and outer core.
b. inner core and outer core.
c. inner core and mantle.
d. crust and inner core.

_____ **6.** The layer that lies just above the outer core of the Earth is the
a. crust.
b. inner core.
c. mantle.
d. Moho.

_____ **7.** Scientists infer knowledge about the Earth's deep interior core from
a. mine shaft rocks.
b. oil well samples.
c. X-ray images.
d. earthquakes.

_____ **8.** Crustal rocks differ from inner core rocks in that they are not abundant in
a. silicon.
b. oxygen.
c. iron.
d. nickel.

_____ **9.** Earthquakes produce and scientists record
a. P and W waves.
b. S and P waves.
c. A and S waves.
d. S and B waves.

_____ **10.** All layers of the Earth are similar in that they contain
a. iron.
b. nickel.
c. silicon.
d. oxygen.

_____ **11**. The best place to drill for samples of rock from the Moho would be through the
a. Rocky Mountains.
b. oceanic crust.
c. floor of the Sahara Desert.
d. continental crust.

_____ **12**. Our lithosphere is
a. made of water.
b. cold near the center.
c. a maximum of 35 km thick.
d. made of soil, sand, and rock.

_____ **13**. The crust of the Earth
a. cannot be seen.
b. is very hot.
c. is thin beneath the oceans.
d. is thicker than the mantle.

_____ **14**. From the center of the Earth to its surface,
a. pressure and temperature decrease.
b. temperature decreases and pressure increases.
c. pressure and temperature increase.
d. pressure decreases and temperature increases.

_____ **15**. The Earth's mantle is
a. less dense than the crust.
b. thicker than the inner core.
c. thinner than the crust.
d. deeper in the Earth than the outer core.

_____ **16**. The liquid layer of the Earth composed of nickel and iron is the
a. crust.
b. outer core.
c. mantle.
d. inner core.

_____ **17**. The crust beneath the oceans is
a. thinner than the crust under continents.
b. thicker than the crust under mountains.
c. less dense than continental crust.
d. covered by a thicker layer of granite than continental crust.

_____ **18**. The reason that iron in the Earth's inner core exists as a solid is its
a. chemical composition.
b. temperature.
c. pressure.
d. volume.

_____ **19**. At a depth of 2900 km, P waves generated by earthquakes
a. move slowly through liquids.
b. fail to pass through liquids.
c. move more slowly than S waves through liquids.
d. move well through liquids.

_____ **20**. The seven lithospheric plates on our planet float on
a. solid granite.
b. the inner core.
c. hot molten material.
d. the outer core.

_____ **21**. The average thickness of oceanic crust is
a. 4 km.
b. 8 km.
c. 12 km.
d. 16 km.

_____ **22**. The Moho is positioned between the
a. mantle and crust.
b. outer core and inner core.
c. mantle and outer core.
d. inner core and mantle.

Name ______________________________ Class ______________ Date ____________

_____ **23.** The inner core can be distinguished from the outer core by its
a. greater thickness.
b. content of iron and nickel.
c. location at 2900 km below the Earth's crust.
d. solid state.

_____ **24.** The presence of a magnetic field in the Earth is believed to be due to
a. magnesium in the Earth's crust.
b. nickel in the outer core.
c. iron in the inner core.
d. silicon in the mantle.

_____ **25.** The Earth's thickest layer is the
a. outer core. c. mantle.
b. Moho. d. inner core.

_____ **26.** The most abundant elements in the crust of the Earth are
a. iron and silicon. c. calcium and aluminum.
b. oxygen and silicon. d. magnesium and oxygen.

_____ **27.** P waves travel
a. easily through solids and liquids.
b. easily through liquids but not easily through solids.
c. easily through solids but not easily through liquids.
d. through neither solids nor liquids.

_____ **28.** Seismic waves are produced by
a. earthquakes. c. heated liquids.
b. heated solids. d. the Earth's magnetic field.

_____ **29.** A solid that has plasticity
a. is at low pressure. c. cannot change shape.
b. is at low temperature. d. can flow.

_____ **30.** Temperatures in the mantle range between
a. 0°C and 870°C. c. 2200°C and 5000°C.
b. 870°C and 2200°C. d. 500°C and 10,000°C.

TRUE OR FALSE

Determine whether each statement is true or false.

_____ **31.** The laser is the instrument used by scientists to measure the waves produced by earthquakes deep within the Earth.

_____ **32.** The boundary that separates the inner core from the mantle is the Moho.

_____ **33.** S waves produced within the Earth cannot pass through liquids.

_____ **34.** The inner core of the Earth has been identified as a dense liquid.

_____ **35.** The mantle is that layer of the Earth which lies above the inner core.

_____ 36. Drilling from the outside of the Earth, you would have to pass through the mantle before your could reach the Moho.

_____ 37. Porosity is the ability of a solid to act like a liquid and change shape.

_____ 38. The crust has been identified as the thinnest layer of the Earth.

_____ 39. Soil, rock, and water are the three forms of matter that are in direct contact with and cover the mantle of the Earth.

_____ 40. The layer of the Earth that accounts for more than 60 percent of the mass of the Earth is the mantle.

COMPLETION

Fill in the word or number that best completes each statement.

_____________ 41. The two types of seismic waves produced by all earthquakes at the same time are P waves and _____ waves.

_____________ 42. The Earth's center is made of two layers called the _____ and the _____.

_____________ 43. An instrument that detects and records seismic waves from within the Earth is the _____.

_____________ 44. The layer of the Earth called the _____ lies just above the outer core.

_____________ 45. Named after a Yugoslav scientist, the _____ separates the Earth's outer crust from the mantle.

_____________ 46. The mantle is made up basically of the elements silicon, _____, magnesium, and _____.

_____________ 47. Great heat and pressure in the Earth cause the materials in the mantle to exhibit the property of _____, in which materials flow and change shape.

_____________ 48. The most abundant elements present in the Earth's crust include oxygen and _____.

_____________ 49. The uppermost solid part of the Earth, called the _____, includes the crust of the Earth.

_____________ 50. _____ rock forms when hot liquid rock from deep within the Earth cools and hardens as it reaches the surface.

_____________ 51. The lithosphere of the Earth has at least _____ major plates that drift on top of hot, molten material below.

_____________ 52. The three types of rock that make up the crust of the Earth include _____, igneous, and sedimentary rocks.

_____________ 53. The average thickness of oceanic crust is about _____ kilometers.

_____________ 54. Most of the Earth's crust is covered by soil, rock, and _____.

______________ **55.** _____ rock forms when igneous and sedimentary rocks are changed by heat, pressure, or the action of chemicals.

______________ **56.** Rocks taken from volcanoes and the ocean floor can be used to study the composition of the _____ layer of the Earth.

______________ **57.** The history, composition, and structure of the Earth are studied by specialized scientists called _____.

______________ **58.** It has been determined from _____ waves that the rock that makes up the mantle of the Earth can move like a thick liquid.

______________ **59.** _____ rocks form when small pieces of rock, sand, and other materials are pressed and cemented together by the weight of the other rock layers.

______________ **60.** Scientists have been able to determine that both layers of the Earth's core are composed of the elements _____ and nickel.

USING SCIENCE SKILLS

Use the skills you have developed in the chapter to answer each question.

61. Draw a diagram showing the location of the mantle, outer core, crust, inner core, and Moho. Label the parts of your diagram.

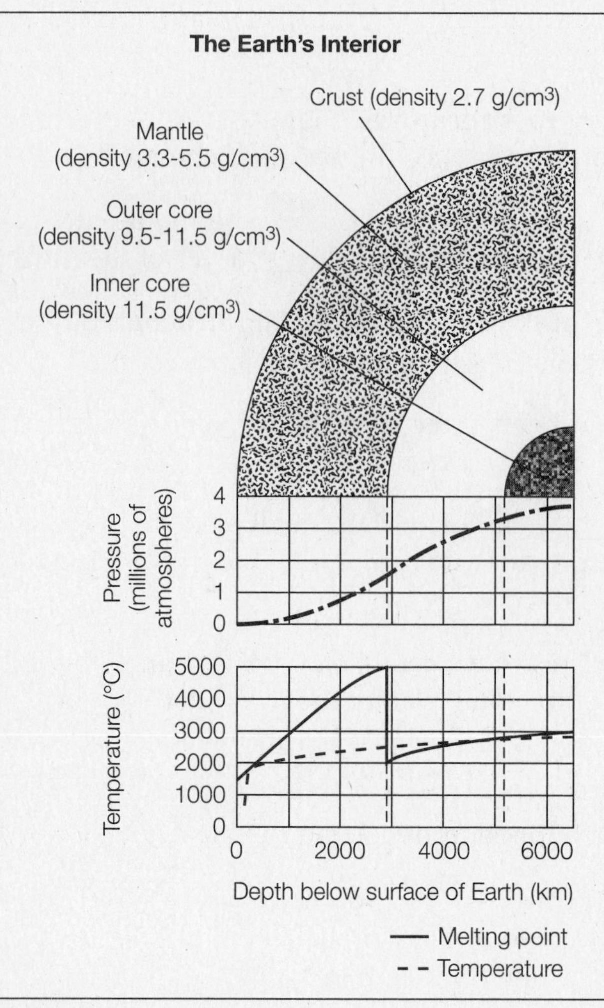

Figure 10

62. In Figure 10, what variable is plotted on the horizontal axis and in what units? On the vertical axis? Which variable is constant?

63. In Figure 10, what is the temperature at a point where the mantle and outer core meet?

64. In Figure 10, how much pressure is there at the deepest part of the inner core?

Name ______________________ Class ____________ Date ____________

65. According to Figure 10, in which layer of the Earth is the temperature greatest?

66. Based on the information given in Figure 10, determine the changes in density, pressure, and temperature from the crust to the center of the Earth.

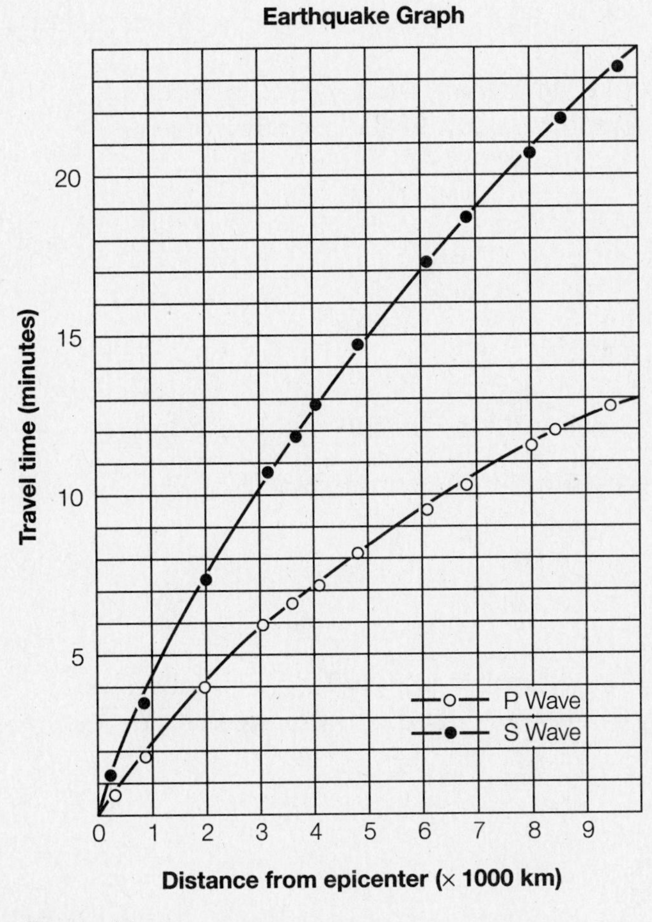

Figure 11

67. What two variables are plotted on the axes of the graph in Figure 11?

68. Where on the graph in Figure 11 is the epicenter of the earthquake represented?

69. How long did it take for the S wave in Figure 11 to travel from the earthquake to a recording station 8000 km away?

70. Based on the data in Figure 11, how far away from the epicenter of the earthquake is the P wave? The S wave?

71. Using the data in Figure 11, determine what the difference in arrival time is between S and P waves at a seismographic station 9000 km away from the epicenter.

CRITICAL THINKING AND APPLICATION

Discuss each of the following in a brief paragraph.

72. If P waves travel 4 km/sec through the mantle, how far will a P wave travel in 3 minutes?

73. The density of material in the Earth's crust is 2.7 g/cm cubed, while the material in the inner core has a density of 11.5 cm cubed. How many times denser than the crust is the inner core?

74. How do we know that the Earth is very hot inside?

Name ______________________________ Class ______________ Date ____________

75. If the Earth's outer core were to change from a liquid to a solid, what effect, if any, would there be on P and S waves traveling through the Earth after an earthquake?

76. How are the inner core and outer core alike? Different?

77. What is the purpose of the drum on a seismograph?

78. In the space provided below, draw and label a typical pattern of P and S seismic waves recorded by a seismograph.

79. Write a short paragraph describing what it might be like immediately following a severe earthquake in a small California town. Describe the town and its people.

80. Study the following story. "Six months ago, a mountain in central Mexico rumbled for the first time in recent history. The mountain, which is an extinct volcano, rumbled again 4 months ago and caused residents of the region to become concerned. Two months later the same volcano rumbled off and on for a 2-day period, then remained quiet. For the past 3 weeks, the mountain has rumbled and shaken the surrounding villages but has not caused any damage." Predict what the events described might be leading to and why.

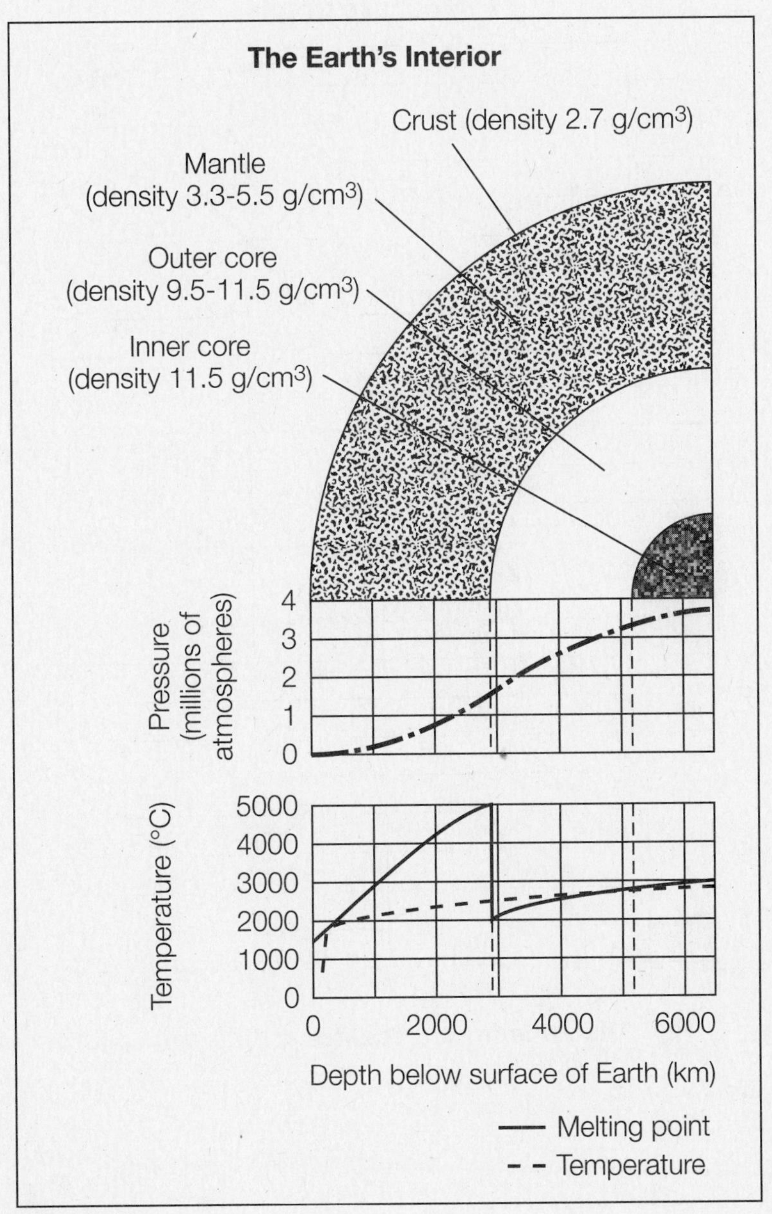
The Earth's Interior
Crust (density 2.7 g/cm3)
Mantle
(density 3.3-5.5 g/cm3)
Outer core
(density 9.5-11.5 g/cm3)
Inner core
(density 11.5 g/cm3)
Pressure
(millions of
atmospheres)
4
3
2
1
0
Temperature (°C)
5000
4000
3000
2000
1000
0
0
2000
4000
6000
Depth below surface of Earth (km)
Melting point
Temperature

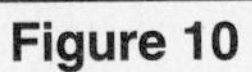

Figure 10

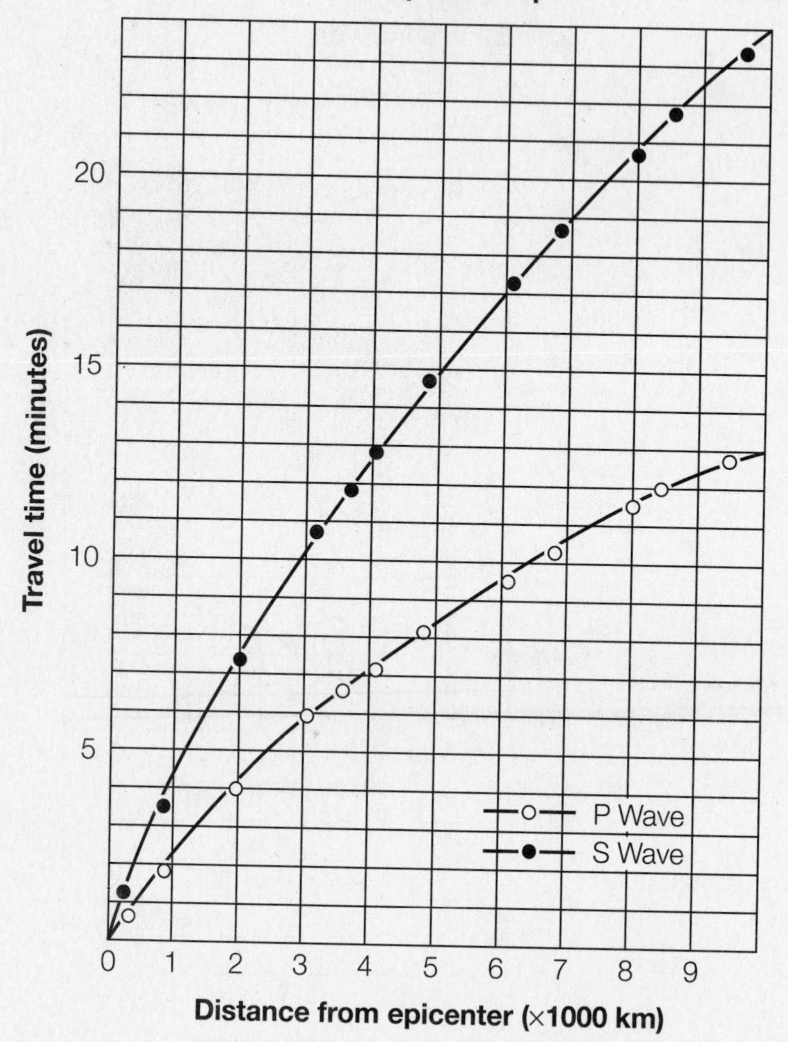
Earthquake Graph
Travel time (minutes)
20
15
10
5
0
1
2
3
4
5
6
7
8
9
P Wave
S Wave
Distance from epicenter (×1000 km)

Figure 11

1. d
2. c
3. c
4. d
5. b
6. c
7. d
8. d
9. b
10. a
11. b
12. d
13. c
14. a
15. b
16. b
17. a
18. c
19. a
20. c
21. b
22. a
23. d
24. c
25. c
26. b
27. c
28. a
29. d
30. b
31. F
32. F
33. T
34. F
35. F
36. F
37. F
38. F
39. F
40. T

41. S
42. inner core, outer core
43. seismograph
44. mantle
45. Moho
46. oxygen, iron
47. plasticity
48. silicon
49. lithosphere
50. Igneous
51. seven
52. metamorphic
53. eight
54. water
55. Metamorphic
56. mantle
57. Geologists
58. seismic
59. Sedimentary
60. iron
61.

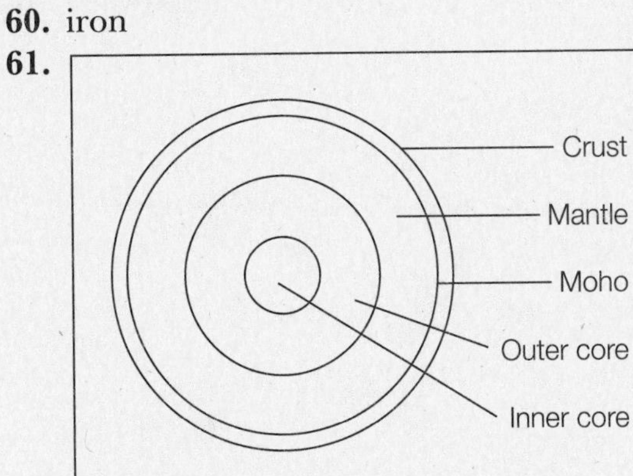

62. Depth is plotted on the horizontal axis in kilometers. Pressure in millions of atmospheres and temperature in degrees Celsius are plotted on the vertical axis. Depth is the constant variable.
63. approximately 2500°C
64. approximately 3.4 million atmospheres
65. inner core
66. temperature, pressure, and density increase
67. distance on the horizontal and time on the vertical
68. 0 time and distance at lower left corner
69. 20.8 minutes
70. P wave approximately 6600 miles; S wave approximately 2800 miles
71. approximately 10.2 minutes
72. In 1 minute, a P wave travels 4 km/sec × 60 sec or 240 km. Therefore, a P wave would travel 240 km × 3 min, or 720 km in 3 minutes.
73. number of times more dense =

$$\frac{\text{density of inner core}}{\text{density of crust}} = \frac{11.5\ \text{cm}^3}{2.7\ \text{cm}^3} = 4.3\ \text{times}$$

74. There are many forms of evidence to support the idea that the Earth's interior is hot. In the midocean ridge, plumes of hot steam rise through vents in the ocean floor. Geysers on the surface of Earth release vast amounts of heat from beneath the Earth, and volcanoes expel huge amounts of melted rock out on the Earth's surface.
75. The P waves would travel much better, and S waves would pass on through the outer core.
76. They are alike in that both are composed of iron and nickel, and are located within the Earth. They are different in that they have different sizes, densities, pressures, and temperatures.
77. The drum of a seismograph is the structure on which seismic waves are recorded. The drum rotates continually.
78.

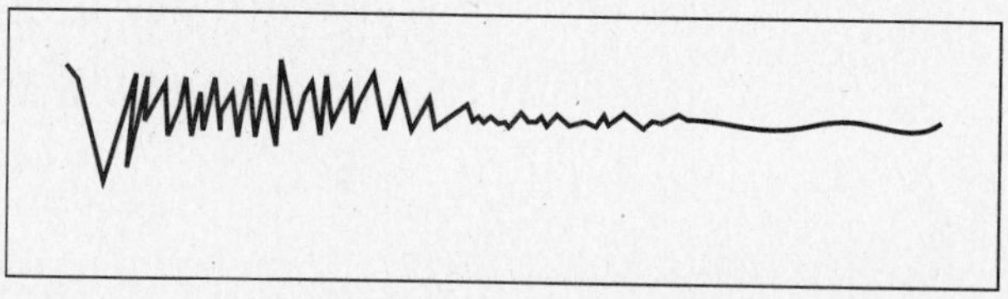

79. Student answers will vary. Typically, students should write about the destruction of buildings, bridges, power lines, and underground water and sewer systems. In addition, mention should be made of injuries and casualties suffered by the citizens of the town. Many people may suffer from shock. If any of the students have actually experienced a serious earthquake, they should write about their own experiences.
80. Student answers may vary. The events described are an indication of volcanic activity that has resumed after a long period of time. Based on the frequency of the rumbling, one might predict that the volcano will erupt again soon, and that appropriate precautions should be taken to protect life and property in the region.

Contents

Performance-Based Tests

Performance-Based Assessment Rubrics

The Performance-Based Tests that follow provide you with an opportunity to evaluate both process skills and student understanding. Unlike methods of assessment that test factual recall, Performance-Based Tests demonstrate students' ability to *think logically*, utilize their *knowledge base*, *organize* their thoughts, and *perform basic skills* inherent to science and every-day life. Because students are not being tested on factual recall, it is important to keep in mind when scoring Performance-Based Tests that a logical and well-thought out answer can be scored just as high as the scientifically "correct" answer. Additional information on the theory behind performance-based assessment, as well as other forms of assessment such as portfolio assessment and oral reports, can be found on pages 76-77 in your Teacher's Desk Reference.

All of the Performance-Based Tests in the Prentice-Hall Science Learning System include one or more assessment objectives among the Teacher's Notes for each test. Using these objectives as the basis for evaluating skill development, the following assessment rubrics have been developed to assist you in your scoring. The rubrics allow for a range of student responses.

■ OUTSTANDING: RATING = 5

Student gives complete responses to all questions; provides a logical explanation for each response; completes all diagrams or data tables; uses descriptive terms accurately; completes the task; and demonstrates an understanding of the basic objectives.

■ COMPETENT: RATING = 4

Student gives complete responses to most questions, but is unable to provide a logical rationale for some answers; completes most diagrams or data tables; uses descriptive terms accurately; and demonstrates an understanding of the basic objectives.

■ SATISFACTORY: RATING = 3

Student gives incomplete answers to some questions and has a vague or limited rationale for answers; does not complete all diagrams or data tables; uses descriptive terms, but not always clearly or accurately; and demonstrates only a general understanding of the basic objectives.

■ UNSATISFACTORY: RATING = 2

Student provides very little response to most questions without any logical rationale for answers; does not complete most diagrams or data tables; does not use descriptive language; and does not exhibit an understanding of the basic objectives.

■ NO ATTEMPT: RATING = 1

Name ______________________ Class ______________ Date ____________

Performance-Based Test

Test 1 Up in the Air

You are a scientist studying the atmosphere of planet Earth. You have been invited to talk to a group of students about some of your research findings.

Check the table in front of you to make sure you have

1. lamp
2. incense stick
3. matches
4. a black stand that surrounds your equipment
5. glass of water

Now you are ready to start.

You plan to start your talk by showing students how balloons are used in scientific projects to study the atmosphere. First you have to determine what the students already know about balloons. You can assume that they have all seen or held a helium-filled balloon. What answer will you expect from students when you ask them why helium-filled balloons float when ordinary balloons do not?

____

____

____

____

____

You are now going to demonstrate another way a balloon can be made to float. With your teacher's permission, light the incense stick. After a few moments blow it out. You should be left with a smoldering tip to the stick. Be careful not to touch the glowing tip with your hand or place it on a surface. Make sure that your breath is not affecting the path of the smoke coming from the tip. Describe what the students observe.

____

____

____

____

Now, switch on the lamp. Allow the surrounding air to be heated by the lamp. What happens to the smoke in the heated air? Place the glowing tip of the incense stick in the glass of water.

Explain what the effects of heat on smoke have to do with hot-air ballooning.

Imagine that a hot-air balloon could continue to rise through the atmosphere. Describe what a passenger in the balloon would observe as the balloon rose through the layers of the atmosphere. Don't forget to name the layers and give some idea of the temperature and other conditions present in each layer.

Name ____________ Class ________ Date ________

One student asked you what a person would need to be able to travel through the layers of the atmosphere. You answer:

The next questions are not so easy but give them a try anyway. In hot-air ballooning you need a gas burner to heat the air in your balloon. What happens when the air outside the balloon becomes less dense? Does this affect the height you can reach? Does the weight of the basket and person become critical at some point? Well, what do you think?

DID YOU KNOW?

Many different types of balloons have been used to study the atmosphere. Superpressure balloons and zero-pressure balloons are the types most often used. These balloons are able to reach great heights, partly because of the enormous volume of air they displace. The larger superpressure balloons have a volume of more than 85,000 cubic meters. Zero-pressure balloons have a volume of about 1.4 million cubic meters. A typical hot-air balloon has a volume of 1700 cubic meters.

Performance-Based Test 1: Up in the Air
Teacher Notes

MATERIALS

desk lamp
source of smoke—a joss stick (incense stick) is perfect
matches
3-sided stand covered in black construction paper
glass of water

PREPARATION

Check that the desk lamp/dissection lamp gives off enough heat. The black-covered stand should be between 60 to 90 cm high; each panel should be between 60 to 90 cm across. The sides of a large cardboard box could be used as well. The stand is to protect the smoke from air currents in the room and to allow students to see the smoke against the black background. You may wish to light the incense stick and hold it yourself. A glass of sand could also be used to extinguish the incense stick. The glowing tip is very hot. Caution students not to touch it or place it on a flammable surface.

OBJECTIVE

The students' understanding of the atmosphere is being assessed.

REFERENCE

Chapter 1, Earth's Atmosphere

Name ____________________ Class ____________ Date ____________

Performance-Based Test

Test 2 Water, Water Everywhere—Yet Not a Glass to Drink

You are an oceanographer with a great deal of experience in desalination techniques (you know how to remove salt from ocean water). Your expertise is much in demand, as fresh water becomes scarcer and as governments in different parts of the world try to find new ways to provide their citizens with water. It is important for your clients to understand the natural processes that replenish the Earth's supply of fresh water, as well as the ways they can make fresh water available to their citizens. Your job today is to explain what you can do for the people of a country with poor supplies of fresh water.

Check the things in front of you to make sure you have

1. beaker
2. test tube
3. Bunsen burner or other source of heat
4. stand and gauze
5. pH paper
6. strong saltwater solution
7. small amount of colored water
8. small amount of fresh water
9. large beaker with ice
10. test-tube holder
11. test-tube rack
12. safety glasses

Now you are ready to start.

You are going to use the equipment in front of you to set up some demonstrations. First, check the pH of the salt-water solution and the fresh water. Record the data in a table.

Put on your safety glasses. Next, take the test tube and pour in a little of the salt solution. Place the test tube in a holder. Heat it. When it is hot and steam is coming off, find a way to collect the steam and test the liquid produced. Explain in words and by a diagram what you have done and why. What happens to the salt solution when it is heated? When you are finished, place the test tube into a rack.

____

____

____

____

____

How does what you have done so far relate to the water cycle?

If what you have been demonstrating was a model of a desalination plant, what would also be produced as a result of the process?

Very carefully, pour a few drops of the colored water into the test tube. Do not shake the tube. What do you observe?

Why does this happen?

What part of the water cycle does this represent? In nature what would happen next?

DID YOU KNOW?

In Egypt 2000 years ago, Julius Caesar used the heat of the sun to distill drinking water for his soldiers.

Performance-Based Test 2: Water, Water Everywhere—Yet Not a Glass to Drink Teacher Notes

MATERIALS

beaker
test tube
Bunsen burner or other source of heat
stand
pH paper
safety glasses
strong salt solution
small amount of colored water
small amount of fresh water
large beaker with ice
test-tube holder
test-tube rack

PREPARATION

Test and record the pH of the liquids to compare them with students' results. The colored water can be made by adding a little food coloring to a test tube of water. Just before class, put the beaker of ice on the table. You may want to perform this demonstration yourself. Follow the suggestions of the class about how to proceed.

OBJECTIVE

Students will explore part of the water cycle and look at the density of fresh and salt water. Understanding of the process and application of the experimental data to the water cycle will be assessed.

REFERENCE

Chapter 2, Earth's Oceans
Chapter 3, Earth's Fresh Water

Name ______________________ Class ____________ Date ____________

Performance-Based Test

Test 3 Off to a Rocky Start

Lately you have been wondering about how rocks are formed. You have decided to try to make some rocks on your own. It seems easiest to make sedimentary rocks, and so you have gathered some things you think you may be able to use to make rocks.

Check the things in front of you to make sure you have

1. petroleum jelly
2. damp sand
3. powdered clay
4. plaster of Paris
5. magnifying glass
6. cake-decorating syringe
7. 2 sedimentary rocks
8. 2 mixing beakers

Now you are ready to start.

Remember that you will have to be able to get your "rocks" out of the press. Smear petroleum jelly on the inside of the barrel of the syringe before you begin production. Write down your ideas. Get the following materials:

damp sand
a mixture of 1 part clay to 3 parts sand
a mixture of 3 parts plaster of Paris and 1 part sand

Make each of your rocks by compressing the mixtures in turn. Examine each manufactured rock and describe what you see. Illustrate your description where possible.

Now examine the two sedimentary rock samples, compare them to your rocks.

Do you think that you have duplicated the formation processes of sedimentary rocks?

If you were to start again, what would you do differently?

DID YOU KNOW?

Most people think of rocks as being solid and hard. It is most surprising therefore to find a sedimentary rock that bends! Because of their crystalline structure, thin slabs of itercolumite—a rare kind of sandstone found in India and North Carolina—can be bent by hand!

Performance-Based Test 3: Off to a Rocky Start Teacher Notes

MATERIALS

petroleum jelly
damp sand
powdered clay
plaster of Paris
magnifying glass
cake-decorating syringe
2 sedimentary rocks
2 mixing beakers

PREPARATION

Provide mixing beakers for the two manufactured rocks. A cutoff syringe is preferable to the cake-decorating syringe because of the tighter fit of the plunger. The syringe needs to be large.

OBJECTIVE

Students will make examples of sedimentary rocks and compare them to actual specimens.

REFERENCE

Chapter 5, Earth's Interior